Times

D1194676

VICTORY!

A Complete, Contemporary Reading Series

Dr. Albert H. Brigance

To order, contact:
Curriculum Associates

5 Esquire Road
No. Billerica, MA 01862-2589

Toll Free: 800 225-0248
(U.S. & Canada)

Phone: 508 667-8000
Fax: 508 667-5706

Copyright © 1991 LinguiSystems, Inc.

ISBN 1-55999-201-8

Editors: Mary McIntyre, Candy McMahon, Lynette Sandrock, Marlowe Bergendoff

Illustrators: Larry Frederick, Margaret Warner, Jim Allen, Patrick Roddy, Tami Schmidt, Brian Rice

Photography: Media Production Services, State of Tennessee Department of General Services

Table of Contents

Officers Keep Crime Off Streets

Despite the age of technology in police work, local police find the traditional officer on the beat is still a valuable means of combating crime. For the past three weeks, there have been extra pairs of feet strolling Main Street and Merchant Park until 11 P.M.

Brian Mayfield, manager of Matson's Market, expressed his appreciation by saying, "I'm delighted with the 3 P.M. to 11 P.M. foot patrol. I'm confident the foot patrol will help combat the crime and destruction we've had in the area in recent months. The officers walking the beat have managed to become part of the neighborhood. Every merchant I've talked with has expressed his sincere appreciation. There's something comforting about a foot patrol, and it's good from a public relations aspect, too."

Lt. Baker, special assignment officer, explains, "We're assigning all new officers to the area for a few weeks. The officers will focus on crime prevention, and the foot patrol puts them in close contact with people. They can stop and ask 'What can I do to help?' or 'How are you doing?' instead of 'What's the problem?' We're stressing the public relations aspect of the foot patrol. Our officers are doing a superior job of fitting into the neighborhoods."

While some people have readily expressed their appreciation for the foot patrol officers, there are others who have not. These include area citizens who aren't well recognized for their law-abiding behavior. They would prefer the officers weren't in the business district. Some of the less law-abiding citizens have been causing crime and destruction in the area. They resent the foot patrol. The police expected this element of opposition.

"Most of our arrests have been for minor crimes," remarks Officer Dale Watson. "But we've encountered more serious crimes, such as purse snatchings and burglaries, too."

Kim Fowler, a foot patrol officer explains, "When we patrol in a car, the criminals seem to be more aware of when we're coming. A car is much easier to see. Foot patrol is much more effective. Criminals never know when we're going to appear at a location. We don't walk the same route or check the same area at a definite time. Suspicious characters seem to resent us."

"When you patrol on foot rather than in a car, it's so much easier to get to know the people," Officer Watson adds. "This aspect of the foot patrol is very good. I feel like an important element in this neighborhood."

"We feel very positive about adding the foot patrol," Lt. Baker said. "There are lots of responses which indicate the law-abiding citizens in the area feel the same way. The citizens seem more certain of their safety when they have to be in the area after business hours. They're assured because the Canton Police Department is on the job. We hope to be a positive influence on citizens who don't always obey the law, also.

"We're a lot like the military," he concluded. "The military has plenty of technology, but it seems there will always be a need for the foot soldier. We're very proud of our men and women officers."

Think It Over

Choose the best answer for each sentence below. Circle the letter of your choice.

1. _____ don't appreciate the foot patrol.
   a. Foot soldiers
   b. Merchants
   c. Citizens who don't obey the law
   d. Police officers

2. Lt. Baker compared the need for the foot patrol to the _____.
   a. military's need for the foot soldier
   b. military's need for high technology
   c. need for more law-abiding citizens
   d. all of the above

3. The officers walking the beat have become part of the neighborhood because _____.
   a. some people resented them
   b. they buy products from the merchants
   c. they wear military uniforms
   d. they get to know the people

4. Criminals don't know when to expect the officers because _____.
   a. the officers don't always walk the same path
   b. the criminals walk the streets when the officers aren't present
   c. the officers don't wear military uniforms
   d. the officers hide from the criminals

5. The main idea of the story is _____.
   a. high technology is an effective way to combat crime
   b. a foot patrol is an effective means of combating crime
   c. it's too expensive for officers to always drive their cars
   d. some people don't appreciate the police officers

Fill It In

Choose a word from the list below that belongs with each group of words.

aspect   technology   element   resent   law-abiding   military

6. Army, soldiers, _____

7. piece, factor, _____

8. take offense, oppose, _____

9. follows rules, legal, _____

10. science, advancements, _____

Word Window

In each of the words below, the *s* sounds like *z*. Read the words and use them in sentences.

applause	beeswax	music	representative
artisan	cruise	phase	resent

You've Got the Beat!

You've been reading about the presence of police officers on city streets. But what effect do you think the officers have had? Your answers to the questions below might give you some ideas.

1. What are some crimes that might be committed in a business district?

    _____

    _____

2. How would the presence of a police officer on foot patrol discourage these crimes?

    _____

    _____

    _____

3. What is your reaction when you see a police officer on the street?

    _____

    _____

4. How is your reaction different from the reaction of a thief?

    _____

    _____

5. Which is more effective, a police officer in a car or a police officer on foot? Why?

    _____

    _____

How would your community be different without police officers?

7

Prisoner Rescues Woman from River

A prisoner on a work-release program from the county jail helped rescue a woman from the Bay Street Bridge Thursday. The woman had been walking across the bridge. The bridge was icy, and she slipped off into the water.

Brian Waters, a prisoner serving a six-month sentence in the county jail, was clearing brush in the park near the river. He saw the terrified woman in the water and immediately dove in to help her as others watched. Because the water was so cold, he didn't have enough energy to pull her completely to the bank. Police officers and firefighters arrived on the scene and completed the rescue.

"Mr. Waters saved the woman's life," a firefighter reported. "She was almost lifeless when we reached her! Mr. Waters helped lessen her chances of drowning."

"I'm not accustomed to swimming in water that cold," Waters said. "I think I could have completed the rescue if I had been in better physical condition. I've been in jail for three months. I haven't been getting enough exercise, and I'm not in very good physical shape.

"For once, I was really pleased to see the police arrive," Mr. Waters continued. "I was getting weak, and the woman looked lifeless."

Witnesses said Waters, age 22, talked to the terrified woman as he tried to swim with her to safety. He encouraged her not to give up.

Ray Whitfield is a guard at the jail. "We started the work-release program for the prisoners about two months ago," he said. "Brian Waters was one of the first who requested to be included in the program. He's done well in the program, and we've come to think of him as a model prisoner.

"This incident is evidence of three things," Whitfield continued. "First, Waters showed

he cares about the community. Secondly, it proves he's not a villain. He's a decent person. Third, it speaks well of the work-release program."

Selected prisoners can qualify for the work-release program when they're within three months of their release dates. While in the program, the prisoners work at regular jobs during the day and come back to the minimum-security section of the jail at night. The program keeps prisoners from becoming depressed and lets them prove they're ready to rejoin society.

The program is designed to help prisoners find work in the community and become a part of it again. Prison officials think it will help prisoners become contributing members of society. Hopefully, it will lessen the chances of them returning to prison.

"If some of the prisoners do well in this program, the judge may release them early," Whitefield said. "We'll make sure the judge knows what Brian Waters did yesterday proves he's not a villain."

"It gave me a great deal of satisfaction to be able to rescue the woman," Waters said. "In jail I've been feeling a little depressed. It's good to have the satisfaction of helping someone. I didn't do it for the sake of publicity or to be a hero. I also didn't do it to impress the judge, but I hope it helps."

Think It Over

Circle the best answer for each sentence below.

1. Brian Waters became part of the work-release program because he was _____.
   a. a hero
   b. a good swimmer
   c. going to be released in four months
   d. none of the above

2. Which happened last? Brian Waters _____.
   a. was satisfied that he could help someone
   b. rescued the woman from the cold water
   c. was permitted to join the work-release program
   d. was in the work-release program

3. Guard Whitfield said the rescue proved _____.
   a. that Brian Waters is a good swimmer
   b. that Brian Waters cares about himself
   c. that some prisoners are villains
   d. the value of the work-release program

4. The woman fell off the bridge because _____.
   a. she was in an accident
   b. the bridge was icy
   c. she wanted to be rescued
   d. she was clumsy

5. The main reason for publishing this story is to _____.
   a. convince the public that not all prisoners are villains
   b. inform readers of Brian Waters' heroic action
   c. inform the public of the value of the work-release program
   d. warn the public of the dangers of icy bridges

Fill It In

Choose a word from the list below that belongs with each group of words.

lessen   depressed   lifeless   terrified   satisfaction   villain

6. pleasure, accomplishment, _____

7. frightened, afraid, _____

8. shorten, reduce, _____

9. sad, discouraged, _____

10. rascal, criminal, _____

Word Window

Each of the words below have the *-less* suffix. Read the words and tell what they mean.

careless   fearless   lifeless   speechless
doubtless   friendless   motionless

Brian's Life

Brian Waters was a hero when he rescued the woman from the river. What do you think his past was like? Write a biography on the lines below that tells about Brian's family, what his crime was, why he committed the crime, why he wanted to be chosen for the work-release program and what might happen to him in the future.

The Life of Brian Waters

_____

_____

_____

_____

_____

_____

_____

_____

_____

_____

_____

_____

_____

How would you feel if an ex-prisoner moved into your neighborhood? Why?

Local Trucker in Caravan

"Bad publicity has damaged the image of the trucking industry. We've got to change that image," said David Ricks, a local trucker.

Ricks is part of a trucking caravan. The caravan will travel across the country next week. The tractor and trailer caravan is a national effort. The drivers hope to portray truckers in a more positive light.

Six rigs will be making the journey from Washington, D.C., to Los Angeles. Ricks will be driving one of the trucks during the week-long trip. Other truckers will join the six rigs along the way.

The destination is an international truck show near Los Angeles. The caravan is sponsored by four tractor and trailer companies. The companies are concerned about the poor image of the trucking industry.

Ricks was selected to be a driver in the caravan. Fellow members of the National Truckers' Association voted for him. The drivers have been named the "All-Star Safety Drivers." Each of the six drivers selected has an excellent safety record. They've been recognized by other drivers for their courtesy. The all-star drivers are dedicated to safe driving. They want to change the image of the industry.

Donald Parks is vice president of King Truck Manufacturing. The company is one of the caravan's sponsors. "Some movie producers have damaged our image," Parks said. "Several movies in the last two years have portrayed truckers as villains. But other movie producers are dedicated to the industry. They've portrayed truckers in a realistic way."

According to the most recent figures available, almost 2,500 people are killed each year in nearly 250,000 car and truck accidents. Approximately 65,000 people are injured in these accidents.

"Let's not put all the blame on the truck drivers," warned Betty Watts of Western Tractor Manufacturing. "Some studies show that 75% of all car and truck accidents are caused by the car driver.

"I admit some people in the industry are unsafe," Ms. Watts continued. "They account for less than 10% of all drivers. That 10% is a serious problem, however. There's an old saying. 'Do something right, and no one remembers; do something wrong, no one forgets.' It's true. That's why we're trying to change our image."

"I've been rolling an 18-wheeler down the road for 16 years. I love it," David Ricks said. "I'm looking forward to this cross-country trip. It will be exciting to reach our destination. I've met three of the other drivers. They're all dedicated drivers. They're safe and courteous. You won't find more professional drivers anywhere. I'm sure the caravan will change people's minds about truckers."

Think It Over

Circle the answer that best completes each sentence below.

1. The purpose of the cross-country trucking caravan is to _____.
   a. change the image of truck drivers
   b. see which truck can make the journey the fastest
   c. discourage movie producers from making movies about truckers
   d. advertise King Truck Manufacturing

2. Which will happen first?
   a. The drivers will have to prove their excellent driving records.
   b. The drivers will leave New York City.
   c. Other truckers will join the caravan.
   d. A movie will be made about the trip.

3. One reason truck drivers have a poor image is _____.
   a. more than 10% of them are villains
   b. most of them are reckless drivers
   c. people remember the bad things they hear about truck drivers
   d. a and c

4. _____ is one of the caravan's sponsors.
   a. Donald Parks
   b. The National Truckers' Association
   c. The All-Star Drivers' Group
   d. King Truck Manufacturing

5. The main reason for publishing this article is to let readers know _____.
   a. the destination of the caravan
   b. what is being done to change the trucking industry's image
   c. that movie producers make poor trucking movies
   d. the trip will take one week

Fill It In

Choose the best word from the list below to complete each sentence.

tractor   dedicate   caravan   portray   destination   trailer

6. *Beginning* is to *start* as *end* is to _____.

7. *Clown* is to *parade* as *truck driver* is to _____.

8. *Horse* is to *wagon* as *tractor* is to _____.

9. *Hide* is to *conceal* as _____ is to *show*.

10. *Devote* is to _____ as *get* is to *receive*.

Word Window

Each of the words below has the *or* sound. Read the words and use them in sentences.

portray	orbit	afford	organize
chord	forbidden	tornado	tortilla

Keep On Truckin'

Would you enjoy driving a truck across the country for a living? Many people enjoy this kind of work. Answer the questions below to get a better idea of the trucking industry.

1. List three negative images you think people have of truck drivers.

_____

_____

_____

2. Do you think these negative images are fair? Why? _____

_____

_____

3. Explain how a caravan might help improve these images. _____

_____

_____

_____

4. Besides organizing a caravan, what could the trucking industry do to overcome their negative

images? _____

_____

_____

5. If you were a truck driver, what three positive qualities would you like to be known for?

_____

_____

_____

Name some jobs related to the trucking industry.

Bald Eagle Shooting Investigated

The Chester County Fish and Wildlife Agency reported that a bald eagle was found dead yesterday in a remote area. The bird had been shot with two bullets at least three days ago. No sightings were made of the killing. The Agency is investigating the shooting.

Officer Robert Walters is heading the investigation. "We have some good leads in the case," he said. "We also have one of the bullets. The bullet may help us find the guilty party."

Allen Bright, Special Agent with the U.S. Fish and Wildlife Service, is helping with the investigation. Anyone with information concerning the incident should contact Officer Walters or Special Agent Bright. A reward of $3,000 is offered for information leading to an arrest.

The Bald Eagle Protection Act was passed in 1962. The act makes it illegal to kill a bald eagle. People found guilty of this crime may be sentenced up to five years in prison. They may also have to pay a fine up to $20,000.

"The person who shot the bird may not have known it was a bald eagle," Bright said. "The bird did not have the white head and tail markings. These markings don't appear until the bird is about four years old. However, these facts don't excuse the killer from the crime."

Agent Bright continued, "The bald eagle is a protected species. It's on the Endangered Species List which means it's protected by federal law."

Anyone who finds the body of a dead bald eagle is required to turn it over to federal authorities. The body of the dead bird is sent to a Fish and Wildlife Service laboratory in Wisconsin where the cause of death is determined.

According to Officer Walters, "The number of people arrested for killing eagles is small, because sightings of bald eagle killings rarely occur. One problem is that an illegal killing usually happens in a remote territory where there is no witness. Unless there's a witness, it's pretty difficult to track down the killer."

The bodies of almost 800 bald eagles have been turned over to the Fish and Wildlife Laboratory in Wisconsin during the past five years. Approximately 20% of these birds are believed to have been victims of bullets from the guns of hunters.

"Another problem with trying to increase the eagle population is the loss of good nesting places and natural habitats," Agent Bright explained. "The bald eagles want to live in isolated habitats. These are becoming harder and harder for eagles to find."

"In the 1950s and 1960s, the chemical DDT was used to kill insects," Officer Walters continued. "This caused a sharp decline in the eagle population. The use of DDT resulted in eagle eggs with very thin shells. Many shells broke easily. Therefore, few eaglets were hatched. Laws passed in 1972 made it illegal to spray with DDT. However, it took several years for the chemical to disappear completely from each isolated territory where it had been used."

"Eagles have enough trouble surviving in today's changing environment," Agent Bright concluded. "It's a shame they have to fear people as well."

Think It Over

Circle the best answer for each sentence below.

1. Whoever shot the bird may not have known it was a bald eagle because _____.
   a. it was in a remote area
   b. it had been flying too high for the person to see
   c. eagles are rarely sighted
   d. it was too young to have the markings of an eagle

2. Which happened first?
   a. The Bald Eagle Protection Act was passed.
   b. DDT was used to kill insects.
   c. 800 bald eagles were sent to Wisconsin.
   d. A reward was offered for information about the shooting.

3. The spraying of DDT added to the decrease in the eagle population because _____.
   a. the poison was so deadly, it killed the bird
   b. it was used to kill insects which the eagles used as food
   c. it caused the eggshells to break easily
   d. the eagles ate plants that had been sprayed

4. Eagles like _____ habitats.
   a. remote
   b. isolated
   c. natural
   d. all of the above

5. The main idea of this story is _____.
   a. it's illegal to kill a bald eagle
   b. DDT is a deadly chemical
   c. an adult eagle has a white head and tail markings
   d. dead eagles are sent to a laboratory in Wisconsin

Fill It In

Choose the best word from the list below to complete each numbered item.

remote   habitats   species   sightings   territory   isolated

6. Do you know how many _____ of animals there are?

7. Industry has ruined some animals' _____.

8. I'd like to explore the _____ north of Canada.

9. Few cougar _____ have been reported in this area.

10. A faraway area could be described as _____.

Word Window

In each of the words below, *-ings* was added to turn a verb into a noun. Read each of the words aloud.

belongings   furnishings   readings   sightings
endings   headings   savings   surroundings

Our Animal Friends

Why would anyone want to shoot an eagle? It's hard to imagine anyone wanting to harm an endangered animal. The questions below will help you think of ways to save our animal friends.

1. What dangers does an endangered animal face? _____

_____

2. What are some of your favorite woodland birds and animals? _____

_____

3. What would you do if you saw someone shooting at one of these animals?

_____

_____

Now, use the space below to write a letter to the person who shot the bald eagle in the story.

 Dear Hunter,

  Your shooting of the bald eagle makes me feel _____

_____. I feel this way because _____

_____.

  I think you should have to _____

_____ for shooting the bird.

        An Animal Lover,

        _____

Recommend a law that applies to the shooting of bald eagles.

Those Proud Marines!

The sergeant silently boarded the bus and stared down the aisle with his cold, hard eyes. In a firm, loud voice he said, "While you are here, you will follow all orders obediently, quickly and willingly. You will be told when to get up, and you will do it quickly. You'll be told when you can hit the sack, and you'll be so exhausted you'll be happy to do so. I won't be your father or your mother. You'll be more obedient to me than you were to them. My job is to be your mental commander, to think for you. Your job is to follow orders. I'm your drill instructor, and I will change all of you into Marines in less than three months!"

Sgt. Ray Sharp paced up and down the aisle of the bus as he recited the regulations of boot camp. The young men and women who had said good-bye to their parents, spouses and friends the day before sat at attention. They were afraid they might miss a regulation that Sgt. Sharp recited.

The newcomers never had anyone talk to them so directly and with such force before. Most had the feeling they had signed on the wrong line, but they realized it was too late.

Sgt. Sharp ended the first encounter with his new group of future Marines with the order, "At this time you will get off the bus. Line up on the yellow footprints painted along the side of the street."

Nearly 40,000 young men and women from 17 to 29 years of age meet someone like Sgt. Sharp each year as they arrive for their Marine boot camp training. They come from big cities, small towns and farms.

Each day and most nights during the next 12 weeks, the newcomers will have many encounters with their Sgt. Sharp. Even when they try their hardest to be 100% obedient, their sergeant will still yell at them and confuse them. Some recruits feel humiliated.

Marine boot camp has changed greatly since Sgt. Sharp completed his training in 1974. At that time, some drill instructors hit trainees and called them names. Regulations now don't allow a drill instructor to hit new Marines or call them names. But the training is still tough and humiliating.

"I won't break regulations," Sgt. Sharp said, "but I have ways of making life miserable for the recruits. I make them so angry they hate me. I know some of them feel humiliated. But it's for their own good and for the good of our country.

"I'll develop strong bodies by driving the men and women to physical exhaustion each day," Sharp continued. "I develop them mentally by pushing them to their mental limits. As they realize that they can meet new challenges, they develop into proud Marines."

Sgt. Sharp doesn't expect each trainee to become a proud Marine. Some just can't adjust to the demanding schedule and rules. Last year nearly 11% left boot camp.

"Those who graduate from boot camp are proud," Sgt. Sharp said. "I recall one man from my last group who grabbed his buddy's arm, and with tears in his eyes, announced, 'I made it. I'm a United States Marine!'"

Think It Over

Circle the best answer for each sentence below.

1. Sgt. Sharp's job is to _____.
   a. change recruits into Marines in less than three months
   b. confuse recruits
   c. decide which recruits will have to drop out
   d. drive the Marines' bus

2. Which is most likely to happen last? The recruits will _____.
   a. learn the regulations
   b. be driven to physical exhaustion
   c. be proud when they reach their goal of becoming Marines
   d. drop out of boot camp

3. Many recruits felt they had signed on the wrong line because _____.
   a. they thought they had signed up for the Navy
   b. they weren't used to being talked to so roughly
   c. they didn't really want to be in the Marines in the first place
   d. b and c only

4. Sgt. Sharp is a drill instructor because _____.
   a. he doesn't like to tell people what to do
   b. he's tall
   c. he has a lot of friends
   d. he wants to help recruits become proud Marines

5. The main idea of this article is _____.
   a. Sgt. Sharp yells at the recruits so much, some of them drop out
   b. boot camp is rough, but it makes strong Marines out of men and women
   c. recruits learn many new regulations
   d. a recruit must be at least 17 years old

Fill It In

Choose a word from the list below that belongs with each group of words.

aisle   humiliated   recite   obedient   regulations   mental

6. thinking, mind, _____

7. dishonored, shamed, _____

8. state, communicate, _____

9. walkway, passage, _____

10. policies, procedures, _____

Word Window

Read each of the title abbreviations below. Say what each abbreviation means.

Sgt.	DDS	VP	RN
atty.	mgr.	MD	asst.

You're a U.S. Marine!

Imagine you've just graduated from boot camp. You're now a United States Marine! Write a letter to Sgt. Sharp telling him what you liked and disliked about your training. Make your letter serious or funny, but be creative.

Dear Sgt. Sharp,

    I'm writing to tell you my feelings about boot camp. Two things I disliked were

_____ and _____

_____.

    Two things I liked were _____ and _____

_____.

    I met some great people in boot camp. They include my new friend _____

_____, who _____

_____. I also had some great adventures. I think I

liked _____ the most because _____

_____.

    I think you are a _____ drill instructor. I feel this way

because _____ and _____

_____.

    The best lesson I learned while in boot camp is _____

_____

I plan to use what I've learned when I become a _____.

Sincerely,

_____

Do you think it's necessary for a country to have a military force? Why?

19

Letters to the Doctor

Dear Counselor,

Six months ago I became engaged to someone I was sure was a wonderful 22-year-old man. His name is Brian. I thought he would be the ideal husband. He gave me a diamond engagement ring, and we had an engagement party.

At the party, we received several generous gifts from our friends. Some of them weren't sure what to buy us, so together they gave us a cash gift of almost $500.

Brian and I agreed to deposit the cash in a savings account. We planned to use it to help with expenses after our wedding. I thought it was the ideal situation.

Last month Brian and I quarreled, and I returned the engagement ring. At that time, I felt we both still loved each other, so I didn't suggest closing the account. Brian didn't say anything about the account, either. I thought he felt the same way I did. I assumed we might still get back, together.

Last week, I received a notice from the bank. It informed me that the account had been closed. Thinking there was a mistake, I rushed to the bank. There was no mistake. I learned that the man I thought was so wonderful had taken all the funds out of the savings account. I had been betrayed. My Mr. Wonderful was really a bum!

Not only was I humiliated, but I was shocked that Brian could withdraw the money without my signature. I contacted the bum who had betrayed me to resolve the matter. Brian insisted he was entitled to the funds since I had betrayed him by breaking the engagement.

I tried to explain that I am as humiliated as he is. I plan to return the engagement gifts to our friends. However, I can't afford to return the cash out of my own pocket. What should I do? Do I consider this a learning experience?

Perhaps this letter will help other couples avoid a sad situation like this.

Sincerely,

Betrayed in Boston

Dear Betrayed in Boston,

Let me express my sympathy for the uncomfortable situation you're in.

Two signatures are required to open a joint savings account. However, only one signature is necessary to withdraw funds from it. It sounds like your savings account was set up for "Mr. or Ms.," not "Mr. and Ms." Therefore, only one signature was needed to withdraw the funds.

It seems that all you can do is chalk this situation up to experience. Try to learn from your costly mistake. Consider yourself lucky that at least you didn't marry him.

Here's a warning to all couples. Banks will set up joint savings accounts that require both people's signatures to withdraw funds. Be sure you ask for this type of account.

Again, you have my sympathy. I wish you better luck in the future.

Sincerely,

Dr. Cravens

Think It Over

Circle the best answer for each sentence below.

1. Because of what had happened, both Brian and the letter writer felt _____.
   a. like bums
   b. horrid and terrified
   c. relieved
   d. humiliated and betrayed

2. Which happened last?
   a. Brian insisted he was entitled to the funds.
   b. A joint savings account was established.
   c. The writer discovered the account had been closed.
   d. Brian withdrew the money from the bank.

3. Brian was able to withdraw the funds because _____.
   a. he was humiliated
   b. he had changed the account to Mr. or Ms.
   c. the account had been opened for Mr. or Ms.
   d. the letter writer had betrayed him

4. The bank made a mistake by _____.
   a. opening the account
   b. requiring only one signature
   c. allowing Brian to withdraw the funds
   d. none of the above

5. The main idea of the letter and its response is _____.
   a. be sure you understand all contracts before you sign them
   b. engaged couples can't trust each other
   c. Dr. Cravens is a sympathetic man
   d. learn from your experiences

Fill It In

Choose the best word from the list below to fill in each sentence.

betrayed   bum   engagement   ideal   signature   sympathy

6. *Pleasure* is to *pain* as _____ is to *indifference*.

7. *Pal* is to *friendly* as _____ is to *lazy*.

8. *Take* is to *picture* as *write* is to _____.

9. *Wonderful* is to *terrific* as *perfect* is to _____.

10. *Interview* is to *job offer* as _____ is to *wedding*.

Word Window

Circle the letters that make the long *a* sound in each of the words below. Then, read the words and use three of them in sentences.

betrayed   delay   getaway   relay

decaying   dismay   playful   slay

Love and Money Lost

Both Brian and Betrayed in Boston were angry and disappointed after they broke their engagement. Imagine you're Brian or Betrayed in Boston. Write a letter to your ex-fiance or to the bank expressing your feelings.

Dear _____,

_____

_____

_____

_____

_____

Sincerely,

_____

Now, write a paragraph explaining how Betrayed in Boston's letter might help other engaged couples avoid making the same mistakes.

_____

_____

_____

_____

How could the bank have helped Betrayed in Boston avoid her problems?

Flu Epidemic Continues to Spread

According to the Iowa Health Department, a flu epidemic hit the state last week. Almost 10,000 people are ill. The flu epidemic is expected to spread.

Dr. Fred Stevens is the chief of the Health Department. On Wednesday, he reported that the epidemic has caused several deaths. It has also led to school closings. Hundreds of students missed school this week.

"We're monitoring the situation very closely," Dr. Stevens said. "There were 9,255 cases of flu reported last week. This compares with 748 cases reported three weeks ago. This proves the flu has spread. It's reached dangerous proportions. I'm uncertain just how many deaths have been caused by the flu this week. Firsthand data is not available. But I do know that the infection is extremely hazardous. The very old and the very young are affected the most.

"Of course, many people who get the flu never report it," Dr. Stevens continued. "We have no way of knowing precisely how many people have the flu. However, the average number of cases this early in the flu season is about 1,500. This year, we're seeing more than six times that number."

Scott County closed its schools for the remainder of the week. More than 25% of their students were absent yesterday. Classes are scheduled to resume next Monday. Dr. Stevens believes school officials made the right decision.

"More school districts may need to close," he said. "I've been monitoring the number of absences. I expect them to increase next week. My firsthand experience tells me that this flu has become a community threat."

Approximately 15% of the students in Madison, Wisconsin were absent on Friday. Principals plan to count absences again early Monday morning. They'll make a decision by noon to close the schools or not.

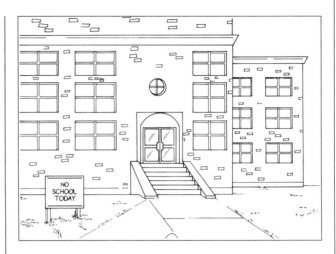

Absences could be more than 20%. If so, school officials will recommend canceling classes for the remainder of the week.

People affected by the flu have similar symptoms. These include headaches, aching muscles, fever, chills and a cough. Anyone with the infection should drink lots of fluids. It's also important to eat healthy foods and get plenty of rest. The very old and the very young should seek medical treatment.

Dr. Patricia Gaines works in the emergency room at Madison General Hospital. She noted, "We've seen a high number of flu cases this week. Our doctors treated almost 500 patients. Ninety-two percent of them were treated and sent home. The remainder stayed in the hospital for at least two days."

The number of cases rose sharply this week. Dr. Stevens said students were returning from a two-week vacation. Some healthy students then came in contact with students who had the infection. They didn't experience symptoms until several days later.

"We'll monitor the flu cases very closely," Dr. Stevens said. "We recommend schools close if absences are high. Many absences mean the flu has reached dangerous proportions."

Think It Over

Choose the best answer for each sentence below. Circle the letter of your choice.

1. The flu infection is extremely hazardous to _____.
   a. about 15% of the students
   b. most of the students who were absent from school
   c. the very old and the very young
   d. state health officials

2. Dr. Stevens believes the reason for the sharp rise in the number of flu cases last week was _____.
   a. students were exposed to the infection after returning from vacation
   b. the students didn't eat properly or get enough sleep during vacation
   c. all the people who had the flu reported it
   d. none of the above

3. More school districts will cancel classes _____.
   a. if at least half the students are ill
   b. if absences are more than 20%
   c. if most of the teachers are sick
   d. if Scott County continues to close its schools

4. The main reason for publishing this article was to _____.
   a. let the readers know what causes the flu and what treatment to use
   b. tell the readers the Health Department would not be monitoring the epidemic
   c. inform parents that school was canceled until Monday
   d. report the progress of the flu epidemic in a news story

5. Dr. Stevens reported that the flu signs include _____.
   a. stomach cramps and sore throat
   b. headache, fever, chills, and aching muscles
   c. lower backache, headache and sore throat
   d. dizziness, sore throat and a cough

Fill It In

Choose the best word from the list below to complete each sentence.

epidemic   firsthand   flu   monitoring   proportions   remainder

6. Let's take the _____ of the cake home and freeze it.

7. Many people stay in bed when they're sick with the _____.

8. A measles _____ rarely occurs today in the United States.

9. I got _____ information about the accident from the reporter.

10. The nurse is _____ the patient's heart rate.

Word Window

All the words below contain the *ir* combination. Read each word and use it in a sentence.

firsthand   admiral   circular   circumstance
stirrup   admiration   fir   whirr

Flu Chart

Madison General Hospital released a chart showing the number of flu cases they treated for the first five days of the flu epidemic. Look at the chart below and then answer the questions.

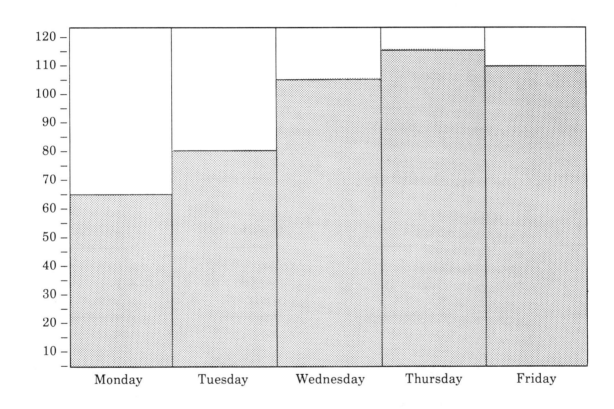

1. How many flu cases did the hospital treat on Tuesday? _____

2. Which day did the hospital treat the most flu cases? _____

3. Which day did the hospital treat the fewest flu cases? _____

4. Which day did the number of flu cases treated go down from the day before? _____

5. Did the number of flu cases go up or down between Wednesday and Thursday? _____

What other illnesses can become epidemics? Why do you think epidemics happen?

Spectators a Problem at Accident Scene

"I'll tell you one thing we don't need at a tragic scene like we had yesterday. We don't need spectators," said Lt. Jenny McDonald of the Dayton police force. "Curious spectators keep emergency people from treating the survivors. The spectators are just in the way. People like to stop to see what happened. When a crowd forms, emergency people can't get through. This means the victims have to wait for treatment."

Lt. McDonald expressed her frustration after yesterday's tragic accident. The accident occurred when two vehicles collided on Highway 52 during a rainstorm.

"We frequently have curious spectators. Yesterday was the worst," Lt. McDonald said. "The spectators created a real hazard. They prevented the survivors from being treated. We're fortunate there weren't more mishaps."

Lt. McDonald continued, "I know people feel a need to express compassion. This type of mishap brings out emotions. But people should take precautions not to create a hazard. They could cause another mishap."

Lt. McDonald recommends these tips to motorists who come upon a car accident.

• If you're trained to handle emergencies or if you're a witness, then stop. The only other time you should stop is if you're the first person to come upon an accident. Otherwise, keep driving.

• If you're the first person on the scene, call the police. Then, try to comfort the victims. Hold their hands and tell them help is on the way. Don't apply first aid unless you're trained. You might cause more injury to the victim.

• Don't move the victims. There are two exceptions. One is if the vehicle is on fire. The other is if the victim is in the path of traffic.

• Try to keep the scene from becoming dangerous. Use your car blinkers to warn traffic. Tie a handkerchief to your car's antenna if you need help. A handkerchief is a signal for a police officer to stop to help.

• When emergency people arrive, let them take charge. Take directions from them. When your assistance is no longer needed, leave the scene.

• Write down facts about the accident. Write down the time of the mishap. Tell the precautions you took. Include any other information you can remember. Note if the survivors were conscious or unconscious.

"In recent years, I've seen many motorists who have wanted to move the victims," Lt. McDonald said. "These motorists have good intentions. But I've seen many victims who were hurt by well-meaning motorists. There's nothing wrong with having compassion for victims. But don't become a spectator. You'll only add to the frustration of the people who are trained to help."

Lesson 8

26

Copyright © 1991 LinguiSystems, Inc.

Think It Over

Circle the letter of the best answer for each sentence below.

1. Lt. McDonald recommends that accident victims not be moved from their vehicle unless
   _____.
   a. they appear to be severely injured
   b. the victim is in the path of approaching traffic
   c. the vehicle is on fire
   d. both b and c

2. The first thing to do when you're the first to arrive at the scene of an accident in which people
   have been injured is to _____.
   a. write down facts about the accident
   b. call the police
   c. make sure all survivors are removed from their vehicles
   d. attempt to clear the way for the arrival of emergency vehicles

3. Curious spectators are not needed at an accident scene because _____.
   a. they keep emergency people from getting through to treat survivors
   b. they might apply first aid
   c. they don't know how to help the victims
   d. they might get too excited and cause another accident

4. You should apply first aid to the victims _____.
   a. if they need it
   b. before the medical people arrive
   c. when the medical people arrive
   d. only if you are trained to do so

5. Another good title for this article would be _____.
   a. When to Apply First Aid
   b. Lieutenant Is Frustrated with Emergency People
   c. Only Stop If You Care
   d. When to Stop at Accidents

Fill It In

Choose the best word from the list below to complete each sentence.

compassion   frustration   handkerchief   mishap   spectators   survivors

6. *Watch* is to *spectators* as *live* is to _____.

7. We could tell from his actions that he was a very concerned person with lots of kindness and

   _____.

8. People who watch a sporting event are called _____.

9. What word goes with *accident, collision, disaster, crash* and *wreck*? _____

10. What word goes with *upset, defeated* and *stressed*? _____

Word Window

Look at the pairs of words below. The second word in each pair ends with -or. Read each word and use it in a sentence.

spectate - spectator   create - creator   survive - survivor   profess - professor
collect - collector   sculpt - sculptor   inspect - inspector   supervise - supervisor

Safety First

Accidents occur at home, school and just about anywhere people work and play. You can help prevent accidents when you know and follow safety rules. For each situation below, list two safety rules you should follow.

At Home in the Bathroom

1. _____

_____

_____

2. _____

_____

_____

At School in the Gym

1. _____

_____

_____

2. _____

_____

_____

When Riding a Bicycle

1. _____

_____

_____

2. _____

_____

_____

When Walking or Jogging

1. _____

_____

_____

2. _____

_____

_____

Where else are safety rules important? Why?

The Hazards of a Toolbox

The police station should be a safe place to leave a toolbox. That's what repair specialist Charles Wise thought. Mr. Wise repairs typewriters. He had repaired six typewriters by 4:00 P.M. yesterday. Before his departure, he checked to see how many more typewriters needed repair.

He thought, "If I come back early in the morning, I can finish this job tomorrow." After sliding his toolbox under a desk, Wise made his departure from the police station.

At 6:15 P.M., Sergeant John Blake answered a call at the dispatch desk. A strange voice which was hard to comprehend mumbled a few words. Then the caller hung up. Sgt. Blake was sure he heard the words "box," "desk," and "go off tonight." But the words were jumbled. Sergeant Blake couldn't comprehend what the caller had said.

Sgt. Blake discussed the call with Sgt. Carl White. They concluded there was really nothing they could do about the call.

During his coffee break, Sergeant Blake walked between two rows of desks on his way to the coffee room. He noticed a strange box under a desk at the end of the aisle. The words "box" and "desk" from the phone call came to mind. He also remembered the words "go off tonight." Then he remembered another sound from the caller's voice — the sound for the letter "b."

"Bomb begins with the letter b!" Sgt. Blake said out loud.

Was the caller saying something about a bomb in a box under a desk that would go off tonight? He wasn't sure if the box held explosives, but he couldn't take the risk.

Sgt. Blake discussed the possible bomb threat with Sgt. White. Then, he called the Emergency Squad. The squad used long ropes to remove the box from the building. The box was placed in a trailer. Then, it was taken to an isolated field on the south side of town.

The Emergency Squad used a small stick of dynamite to blast the box. To the officers' relief, the box didn't contain explosives. But the dynamite blasted most of the items in the box beyond recognition. The officers never discovered who made the mysterious phone call.

Mr. Wise arrived at the police station promptly the next morning with hopes of repairing the last of the typewriters. But he couldn't find his toolbox. After searching under several desks, Wise asked the sergeant at the front desk if he had seen the toolbox.

"When the sergeant told me they had blown my toolbox to bits, I couldn't believe it," Wise said. "I thought it was a joke. From now on, I'll tell the officers what I'm leaving at the station and why."

Circle the answer for each sentence below.

1. Sgt. Blake noticed a strange box _____.
   a. under a desk in the break room
   b. under the dispatcher's desk
   c. in the middle of the aisle
   d. none of the above

2. Which happened last?
   a. Sgt. Blake went for a cup of coffee.
   b. A caller left a message Sgt. Blake couldn't understand.
   c. Charles Wise thought the police officers were kidding him.
   d. The toolbox was blown up.

3. The Bomb Squad came to the police station because _____.
   a. Sgt. Blake told them there was a bomb there
   b. a caller said there was a bomb at the police station
   c. Sgt. Blake thought there might be bomb in a box
   d. they wanted to blow the toolbox to pieces

4. Mr. Wise left his toolbox at the station because _____.
   a. he would need it the next morning
   b. he wanted to see what the police would do with it
   c. he was lazy and didn't want to take it home
   d. he's a typewriter repairperson

5. Another title for this story could be _____.
   a. Repairperson Can't Complete the Job
   b. Bomb Squad Blows Up a Toolbox
   c. Bomb Discovered After Mysterious Call
   d. Repairperson Is Without Tools

———— **Fill It In** ————————————

Follow the directions below. When you're finished, each column should add up to 40.

6. If *dynamite* is safe to play with, put a 10 in box 11.

7. If you use a *typewriter* to learn how to spell, put a 16 in box 8.

8. If you make a *departure* from a building when you leave, put a 12 in box 9.

9. If a *bomb* is destructive, put an 18 in box 10.

10. If *comprehend* means *to question* put a 10 in box 7.

11. If secretaries use *typewriters*, put an 11 in box 7.

12. If you *comprehend* the directions for this page, put a 15 in box 8.

13. If *explosives* cause damage, put a 14 in box 6.

6.	9.
7.	10.
8.	11. **10**

Word Window

In each of the words below, the *y* has the long *i* sound. Say the words aloud.

by	dying	nylon	tying
cypress	dynamite	recycle	typewriter

Rules Are Rules

How could the police have prevented the misunderstanding about the toolbox? Maybe the police department needs some rules for visitors. Use the spaces below to write some rules for visitors to the police department.

Visitors' Rules

1. _____

2. _____

3. _____

4. _____

5. _____

6. _____

7. _____

8. _____

9. _____

10. _____

Some people will want to know why the police department has these rules. On the lines below, explain why you wrote three of these rules. Write the number of the rule in front of your explanation.

_____

_____

_____

_____

_____

_____

Game Show Contestants

The popularity of game shows in America has been unbelievable in recent years. Game shows can be viewed on almost every TV station. They're shown in the morning, in the afternoon and in the evening during prime viewing time.

As game shows become more popular, more people are eager to appear on them. They want to be in the spotlight in front of millions of viewers. Every year, half a million people compete for a spot on a game show. They submit applications months in advance. However, game show producers are desperate for qualified, enthusiastic players.

"We're desperate for outgoing, radiant contestants," said one producer. "They need to be able to stand in the spotlight and think on their feet. They also need to speak English well. We're so desperate for players that we're going to other countries looking for qualified people. Anyone we choose must speak English."

"The lack of qualified people is our biggest frustration," reported another producer. "We're interviewing 75,000 people across the country to find quick thinkers with bright personalities. We'll ask the people we choose to appear on the show next year."

"With some programs, another frustration is trying to find sponsors," he continued. "That's not true with our show. Its popularity is so great, big companies are begging us to be our sponsors. They're anxious to have their products seen by a viewing audience of 50 million people."

What's the best way to be selected from thousands of people competing to be in the spotlight? Sam Greer interviews several thousand would-be television personalities each year. "First," he advised, "choose your favorite show. Decide if you play it well and if it suits your personality. Then, play along as you view it at home. Invite family members and friends to practice the game with you.

"Watch the people competing on the show," he added. "Do they have beaming smiles? Do they have radiant personalities? Do they become excited when they answer the questions? The answer to these questions will probably be yes."

"When you're sure which game you want to play, submit your application," Sam Greer continued. "Be prepared if you are invited for an interview. Plan to dress, talk and act just as you would if you were going for a job interview."

Brad Meyer hosts a popular show. "I really love hosting our show," he said. "It's great to see an enthusiastic guest walk onto the stage. That's when I know we're going to have a great show. It makes my job of hosting a lot easier."

Why are would-be players so eager to be on game shows? "That's a question with many answers," said Ray Silvers, a producer. "Many people dream of the luxury of an expensive car or a trip to a foreign country. Others hope to win enough money to be rich for the rest of their lives. Many want to stand in the spotlight for 30 minutes and have that once-in-a-lifetime chance to win big!"

What's your reason for wanting to be on a game show? Is it fame, money or prizes? Whatever the reason, you can dream of being a winner. But remember, 500,000 other Americans have the same dream.

Think It Over

Circle the answer that best completes each item below.

1. Which is not a requirement for a game show contestant?
   a. good English-speaking skills
   b. an outgoing personality
   c. American citizenship
   d. preparation

2. The greatest frustration for many producers is finding _____.
   a. sponsors
   b. qualified contestants
   c. English-speaking players
   d. an audience

3. The first thing a would-be contestant should do is _____.
   a. submit an application
   b. have an interview with a producer
   c. practice playing the game
   d. choose his favorite show

4. Producers look for players from other countries because _____.
   a. they're desperate for players
   b. people from other countries are outgoing
   c. sponsors prefer players from other countries
   d. both a and c

5. The main idea of this article is _____.
   a. contestants who meet producers' requirements are hard to find
   b. there are so many game shows, almost anyone can be a guest
   c. people from other countries are trying to get on game shows
   d. producers have trouble finding sponsors

Fill It In

Choose the best word from the list to complete each sentence below.

English   enthusiastic   host   radiant   submit   would-be

6. My daughter gave me a _____ smile when I came home.

7. The girls' soccer team is _____ about tonight's game.

8. _____ is spoken in many countries of the world.

9. Uncle Greg will _____ the graduation party.

10. _____ your job applications by 2:30 P.M.

Word Window

Review the skills you've learned in Lessons 1 through 9. Read the words aloud.

applause	belongings	admiration
cruise (1)	savings (4)	firsthand (7)
careless	RN	spectator
speechless (2)	Sgt. (5)	supervisor (8)
forbidden	decaying	cycle
tornado (3)	delay (6)	tying (9)

Lights! Camera! Action!

Fame and fortune are two reasons game shows are regaining popularity. Answer the following questions about game shows and you'll be a winner!

1. Give two more reasons why TV game shows are so popular. _____

   _____

   _____

2. What do you like most about TV game shows? _____

   _____

   _____

3. What do you like least about them? _____

   _____

   _____

4. Which person in your family do you think would make the best contestant in a TV game

   show? _____

5. What are your reasons for choosing this person? _____

   _____

   _____

6. Which do you think would be scarier, trying out for a game show or appearing on one? Why?

   _____

   _____

   _____

What game show would best fit your personality? Why?

34

Poor Grades May Cancel Season

"Do your grades average C- or better? Have you passed your physical exam? If so, Coach Evans needs you." Scott County High School students heard this bulletin when they returned from summer vacation.

During the summer, the school board established a rule raising the grade standards for athletes. The new standards require all students to earn a grade average of at least C- before they can play any sport for Scott County High School.

Football Coach Jerry Evans is disappointed with the new standards. "We were destined to have the best football team we've had in many years," he said. "Under these new standards, most of the team isn't qualified to play. Now, it looks like we're destined to have the weakest team we've ever had. My sympathy is for the players. Some are eager to play. But with a grade average of less than C-, many of the players don't meet the new standards."

Coach Evans is attempting to muster enough qualified athletes for a team. Posters on the bulletin boards say, "Keep the Lions alive! Sign up for football!"

According to Coach Evans, it's been very difficult to find enough players for a winning team this year. "Less than half of our returning players have a C- average," he explains. "We need to rebuild our team. We need to muster enough students who can pass the physical examination and make the qualifying grades. If we can't, there's a possibility we'll have to cancel our games for this season."

Scott County's coaches began discussing the new standards as soon as they heard the school board's ruling. Boys' basketball coach Todd Ward agreed with Coach Evans. "The basketball team's destiny is bleak, too," he said. "Four of last year's players are returning this year. Only two of them have grades that qualify them to play under the new standards. The other players will have to improve their grades. They don't have much time. We start practice in October."

"The destiny of the girls' softball team isn't as bleak as that of the football team," said girls' softball coach, Fay Mills. "Practice doesn't begin until after the first grading period. Some of the girls who want to play have low grades now, but there's time for them to improve their grades by then."

Many students with low grade averages have talked to Counselor Fred Byers. "Sports mean so much to them," said Mr. Byers. "I'm sure most of them will make the effort to improve their grades enough to qualify. We'll work closely with them. We'll help every student who asks. I believe all students can earn at least a C- grade average. Maybe the destiny of the Scott County Lions isn't as bleak as it appears."

"The new grade standards were not developed to hurt the sports program," Principal Erica King said. "They're meant to help students get a good education. Playing sports is important to students. However, the knowledge students acquire in the classroom is much more important to their future success. It's important that students rebuild their grades before they rebuild their teams."

Think It Over

Circle the letter of the answer which best completes each sentence.

1. The destiny of the football team appeared bleak because _____.
   a. not enough players could pass the physical examination
   b. not enough players could meet the grade standards
   c. not enough students wanted to play on the team
   d. the school board wanted to get rid of the football team

2. Fay Mills felt that the destiny of the softball team was less bleak than the football team's destiny because_____.
   a. she was a better coach than Coach Evans
   b. all of the girls on the team earned good grades
   c. the new standards didn't apply to softball teams
   d. the girls would have enough time to improve their grades

3. Coach Evans is attempting to get qualified players for his team by _____.
   a. helping students study for their tests
   b. talking to the girls' softball team
   c. putting posters on bulletin boards to promote football
   d. sending letters to the students' parents

4. According to Counselor Byers,_____.
   a. athletes can earn a C- grade average
   b. help will be given to students who need it
   c. the teams' destinies aren't as bleak as they appear
   d. all of the above

5. The main idea of this article is that _____.
   a. athletes will have to earn at least a C- grade average to play sports
   b. Coach Evans is disappointed in his team
   c. the softball team makes better grades than the football team
   d. Coach Evans is trying to muster up qualified athletes

Fill It In

Choose the best word from the list to complete each sentence below.

bleak   bulletin   destined   destiny   muster   rebuild

6. It was difficult for Charles to _____ enough courage to jump from the diving board.

7. Everyone listened carefully to the news _____ forecasting the coming storm.

8. Vickie knew she was _____ to become a ballerina in the future.

9. It took a great amount of time and money to _____ the town after the tornado struck.

10. The winter sky looked _____ and dreary.

36

Word Window

Circle the prefix *re* in each word below. Practice reading the words silently.

reassure   rebound   rebuild   regain
resound   restore   retell   review

Grade Graph

Principal Erica King decided to discover how people felt about the new grade standards. She wants to present the information to the school board at their next meeting. Use the graph below to answer the questions.

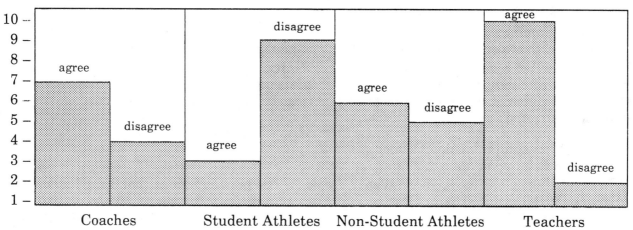

1. How many coaches agree with the standards?

    _____

2. How many teachers don't agree?

    _____

3. Do more student athletes or more nonathletic students agree with the standards?

    _____

4. In which group do the most people agree with the standards?

    _____

5. In which group do the most people disagree with the standards?

    _____

6. What reason do you think the group in question four would give for agreeing with the standards?

    _____

Which two bars of the graph are closest in height? Why are they similar?

Wrong Place, Right Time

State News

A Sunrise Airline jet landed right on time last Monday evening. However, it landed at the wrong airport!

The Sunrise Airline flight originated in Denver. Jackson Airport was the flight's destination. Instead, it landed eight miles away at the smaller Whiteside County Airport.

Dave Carter from the Federal Aviation Administration (FAA) is conducting an investigation of the landing. Mr. Carter said, "I've examined the training and flight record of the pilot very closely. He wasn't an inexperienced kid. He was a middle-aged pilot with many years of aviation experience. I don't believe it was his fault the plane veered off course.

"I recall two similar incidents which occurred in this region," Mr. Carter added. "Three different pilots have landed their airplanes at the wrong airport. It is very unlikely that all three pilots would make the same error in judgment. I believe that the causes of all three incidents originated with an interference in communication."

James McDonald, the vice president of Sunrise Airline, is also investigating the landing. Mr. McDonald said, "I agree with Dave Carter. I think this incident was caused by an interference in communication. I plan to have the equipment in the Jackson Airport control tower checked by an expert. I'll also have the equipment in the Whiteside County Airport checked. The pilot received incorrect information from one of the control towers."

The pilot, who preferred to remain nameless, was interviewed as part of the investigation. "I realized we were at the wrong airport as soon as we were close enough to see the runway," the pilot said. "The Whiteside County Airport runway is 3,966 feet long. That's about half the length of the Jackson Airport runway. When I realized we weren't in Jackson, I decided that landing was the safest thing to do. I

didn't know what was at the end of the short runway. I wasn't sure I could get the airplane back into the air before it collided with something."

Some of the passengers were also interviewed. Most passengers said they hadn't realized anything had happened until they were on the ground. Many passengers said they were grateful just to have landed safely. However, some of them were angry to be delayed.

"We had to stay on the airplane for an hour until a roll ladder was sent from Jackson Airport," complained one middle-aged man. "And now we have to take a bus to Jackson Airport! I'll be hours late by the time I reach my final destination. I wish they would have let us exit on the emergency slide."

The pilot explained that a roll ladder is the safest way to exit an airplane. "That's why the slide is used only for emergencies," he stated. "I felt the safety of my passengers was worth the wait."

Mr. Carter agreed. "The pilot used good judgment in landing the airplane at Whiteside County airport. It was also a good decision to wait for the roll ladder. Some passengers have complained about the delay. I think they should be thanking the pilot for his quick thinking."

Mr. McDonald apologized to the delayed passengers. "Sunrise Airline will make sure this doesn't happen again," he assured them. "We'll determine why the airplane veered off course. We do know one thing for sure. This is definitely a case of being at the wrong place at the right time!"

Lesson 12   38   Copyright © 1991 LinguiSystems, Inc.

Think It Over

Choose the best answer to complete each sentence. Circle the letter of your choice.

1. The pilot of the Sunrise flight from Denver planned to land at the _____.
   a. Denver International Airport
   b. Whiteside County Airport
   c. Jackson Airport
   d. Federal Aviation Administration

2. After landing at Whiteside County Airport, the passengers waited on the plane _____.
   a. for an hour
   b. for a roll ladder to arrive
   c. for a safe exit from the plane
   d. all of the above

3. The pilot knew he was at the wrong airport when _____.
   a. the co-pilot informed him that the plane had veered off course
   b. he saw the short runway
   c. he was contacted by the Federal Aviation Administration
   d. the passengers complained

4. Which happened last?
   a. A roll ladder was sent from Jackson Airport.
   b. The pilot decided to land at Whiteside County Airport.
   c. The flight originated in Denver.
   d. Passengers were told they had landed at the wrong airport.

5. Another title for this story could be _____.
   a. Passengers Exit Plane on Emergency Slide
   b. Airplane Misses Correct Airport by Eight Miles
   c. New Vice President Named for Sunrise Airline
   d. Whiteside County Airport's Runway Is Shortened

Fill It In

Choose the word from the list below that belongs with each group of words.

aviation   interference   investigation   middle-aged   originated   veered

6. disturbance, break, _____

7. began, started, _____

8. swerved, turned, _____

9. mid-life, between young and old, _____

10. study, exploration, _____

Word Window

Read the words below. Circle the *-ence* suffix in each word.

conference   confidence   correspondence   existence

interference   occurrence   reference   residence

Where?   When?

Read the airline schedule below for New Orleans Air carefully. Then, use it to answer the questions.

Flight Number	Departure	Destination	Arrival Time
233	6:03 A.M.	Chicago	8:03 A.M.
703	2:24 P.M.	Orlando	4:00 P.M.
888	4:44 P.M.	Chicago	6:44 P.M.
921	6:38 P.M.	Orlando	8:14 P.M.

1. When does the first flight to Chicago take off? _____

2. Where would flight number 703 take you? _____

3. What is the destination of the flight that leaves the airport last? _____

4. What flight number arrives at its destination last? _____

5. Laurie wants to take the latest possible flight to Chicago. What flight number does she

    want to take? _____

6. What is the destination of the two flights that take two hours? _____

Why do travel agents need airline schedules?

Ex-player Describes Cheers, Jeers

"Go for it!" advised ex-player Jenny Wheeler to "want-to-be" football players Erin Wise and Rebecca Butler. "However, think carefully about it first. You have to be sure you are ready. You have to be prepared for the cruelty that goes with the territory."

Jenny Wheeler had experienced what Erin and Rebecca hoped for. She made history in 1984 when she became the first girl in the county to play football on a boys' team. She played in several games as an eighth grader. Twice she even carried the ball to score game-winning points.

Erin Wise and Rebecca Butler recently requested permission to try out for the Central High School football team. Coach Taylor was very concerned about granting this permission. He asked Jenny to join his meeting with the two hopeful players. "I respect your opinion as an ex-player," he explained.

"I think we're ready," said Erin. "We play football with the guys in our neighborhood. We know it's a rough game, but we're good players."

"I was prepared for the rough physical treatment, too," said Jenny. "However, I wasn't ready for the mental cruelty. You have to be prepared for the jeering. I'm sure the neighborhood guys are more courteous to you than the football fans will be."

What surprised Jenny was the rude treatment she received when she joined the football team. Many of the fans in the bleachers were ex-players. They didn't want a girl on the team so they had no mercy on Jenny. "Most of the jeering was from people who didn't even know me," Jenny said. "However, some of the remarks came from my own classmates.

"There was a good side to my football career," Jenny remembered. "I loved playing and I made many friends on the team. Most of the guys on the team were courteous and

friendly. They knew that I'd do my best to help the team. Unfortunately, there were some players who didn't understand my love for football. They thought I was on the team just to get recognition."

Jenny said her name was often in the headlines. "I didn't ask for all the publicity, but it made some of my teammates angry. They thought I played football just to get my name in the headlines," she explained.

"We don't expect mercy and we're ready for any jeering," said Rebecca. "Don't you think we should be allowed to play as you were?"

"I played football in eighth grade. You want to play in high school," answered Jenny. "I think the mental and physical roughness will be worse for you at the high school level. When I was in high school, I decided to play girls' basketball instead of football. I think it was a good decision. On the girls' basketball team, I was still in the headlines. However, my teammates and fans were cheering instead of jeering.

"I can't make your decision for you," Jenny added. "However, I can tell you what to expect. You'll play with both courteous teammates and those who show no mercy. You'll hear both cheers and jeers. You'll have to do what's right for you. Whatever sports you decide to play, you'll hear me cheering from the bleachers."

41

Think It Over

Choose the best answer to complete each sentence below. Circle the letter of your choice.

1. _____ wanted to play high school football.
   a. Jenny Wheeler
   b. Erin Wise
   c. Rebecca Butler
   d. both b and c

2. Jenny wasn't ready for the _____ she received when she played football.
   a. rough physical treatment
   b. mental cruelty
   c. college scholarships
   d. poor grades

3. Most of the guys on Jenny's team were _____.
   a. rude
   b. better players than she was
   c. courteous and friendly
   d. cruel

4. In high school, Jenny _____.
   a. played on the girls' basketball team
   b. played on the boys' basketball team
   c. played on the boys' football team
   d. started a girls' football team

5. Another title for this story could be _____.
   a. Girls' Football Team Organized
   b. Basketball Star Wins Fourth Championship
   c. Ex-player Advises "Want-To-Be" Players
   d. Coach Taylor Decides Fate of Team

Fill It In

Choose the best words from the list to complete the story below.

bleachers   courteous   ex-player   headlines   jeering   mercy

Hank Frazier played on the basketball team when he went to West High School. Now that he has

graduated, he watches the games from the 6. _____. He was

enjoying Friday night's game until a rude man sat next to him. The man was 7. _____

the West High Wildcats and throwing popcorn. Suddenly, the rude man began to choke on his

popcorn. Hank Frazier was quick to save him. The next morning, the newspaper 8. _____

read, "9. _____ Shows 10. _____."

Word Window

Circle the prefix *ex-* in each word below. Think about the meanings of the words with and without the prefix.

ex-banker   ex-choreographer   ex-firefighter   ex-missionary
ex-player   ex-president   ex-senator   ex-thieves

Cheers and Jeers

Some of the comments that Jenny heard from football fans are written below. Read each comment and decide if it is a cheer or a jeer. Write the word *cheer* or the word *jeer* in front of each comment.

_____ "Good catch, Jenny!"

_____ "Girls can't run! She'll be tackled for sure!"

_____ "Go home, Jenny. You don't belong on the football team!"

_____ "Run, Jenny! You can make it!"

_____ "Aw, Jenny, you missed the ball again! You can't catch!"

_____ "Good try, Jenny! You'll get the next one!"

_____ "Go! Go! Go! I know you'll win the game!"

Think of the three jeers written above. Rewrite each of the jeers to turn it into a cheer that would encourage Jenny.

_____

_____

_____

_____

_____

How would it feel to hear cheers? How would it feel to hear jeers?

Seeing Eye Dogs

Imagine you're a blind pedestrian on a busy street. You can hear the sounds of the traffic. You can sense unseen dangers all around you. You feel like you're in the middle of a battlefield. Now, imagine you have the companionship of a faithful friend. Your friend guides you safely through the dangers of the busy street.

Since World War I, dogs have been the faithful friends who guide many blind people through the dangers in their lives. Many soldiers lost their eyesight during World War I. Without their eyesight, everyday situations became as terrifying as time on the battlefield.

People in Germany began training German shepherd dogs to guide these blind soldiers. German shepherds were chosen for the training program because they had proven their intelligence by learning to herd farm animals. The German shepherd also had the ability to form a close companionship with its master. This was another important quality because a guide dog and his master must work closely as a team.

Today guide dogs are often called Seeing Eye dogs. Seeing Eye dogs are no longer trained only in Germany. Many schools, such as the New Jersey Seeing Eye Dog School, exist in the United States.

In these schools, the dogs are trained to help their masters deal with many situations. For example, a Seeing Eye dog is trained to stop on curbs when guiding a pedestrian. The dog won't allow its master to cross streets until it's safe.

In New Jersey, a 4-H club made this training process easier. Each club member adopted a future Seeing Eye dog. The club members cared for the young dogs until the dogs were a year old. They taught the dogs to be obedient in many situations. The club members also taught the dogs to be good companions. After spending this time with the 4-H members, the dogs were much easier for the Seeing Eye Dog School to train.

Most dogs complete the Seeing Eye training in three months. Then, they meet their future masters. People who need Seeing Eye dogs also come to the school to be trained. The masters and dogs are taught to work as partners. They have a chance to develop a very important feeling of companionship. This feeling makes it easier for the masters to depend upon their dogs.

Many blind people depend on their Seeing Eye dogs to guide them everywhere. This used to cause a problem in some businesses. Some business owners didn't want to allow any dogs in their businesses. A federal law was passed to handle this problem. Now, it's illegal to prevent a Seeing Eye dog from accompanying its master into a business. Business owners who don't allow Seeing Eye dogs in their businesses are subject to a $500 fine. Of course, most people don't mind guide dogs in places where regular dogs aren't allowed.

Without a Seeing Eye dog, a blind person has to depend on another person for many things. A Seeing Eye dog can help a blind person become more independent. It's easier for a person to adjust to life without sight if they can still live independently. For many blind people, a Seeing Eye dog is truly a person's best friend!

Think It Over

Choose the best answer to complete each sentence below. Circle the letter of your choice.

1. People began training guide dogs _____.
   a. after World War I
   b. in Germany
   c. to help soldiers who had lost their eyesight
   d. all of the above

2. German shepherds are often used for Seeing Eye dogs because of their _____.
   a. exceptional eyesight
   b. intelligence
   c. ability to protect their masters
   d. their experience as police dogs

3. 4-H clubs have made Seeing Eye dog training easier by _____.
   a. donating money to the training schools
   b. helping blind people who don't have dogs
   c. adopting and teaching young dogs
   d. teaching masters to work with their dogs

4. A federal law states that Seeing Eye dogs must _____.
   a. be allowed in businesses
   b. be kept on leashes
   c. be trained for three months
   d. be German shepherds

5. This story was written to tell people about _____.
   a. the 4-H club
   b. the law that makes it illegal to let a dog into a business
   c. Seeing Eye dogs
   d. German shepherds and other helpful breeds of dogs

Fill It In

Follow the directions below. If you fill in the puzzle correctly, both rows will add up to 44.

6. If *Germany* is a country in Europe, put a 30 in box 6.

7. If a *pedestrian* rides in a car, put a 23 in box 7.

8. If *shepherds* are in charge of watching sheep, put a 7 in box 7.

9. If *companionship* is like *friendship*, put a 22 in box 9.

10. If *German* chocolate is named for Germany, put an 11 in box 10.

11. If *Germany* is in the United States, put a 32 in box 10.

12. If a *battlefield* is a peaceful place, put a 21 in box 9.

13. If a war occurs on a *battlefield*, put a 7 in box 8.

6.	9.
7.	10.
8.	11.
	11

Word Window

Circle the suffix -*ship* in each word below. Practice reading the words and using them in sentences.

apprenticeship   championship   companionship   citizenship

friendship   membership   relationship   scholarship

Helpful Animals

Seeing Eye dogs aren't the only animals that help people. You may have read about other helpful animals, like Hearing Ear dogs. Some animals provide people with food, transportation and companionship. Think about the animals listed in the box. Next, write each animal's name in the list where it belongs. Then, think of another animal to add to each list. Finally, answer the questions below.

bee	camel	cat	chicken
cow	dog	donkey	elephant
hamster	horse	parakeet	turkey

Food	Transportation	Companionship
_____	_____	_____
_____	_____	_____
_____	_____	_____
_____	_____	_____
_____	_____	_____

1. Which animal from the lists is the most helpful to people? Why?

   _____

   _____

2. Is it more important for animals to provide food, transportation or companionship? Why?

   _____

   _____

3. Some animals are helpful in other ways. They help people do their work. Think of as many animals as you can that help people with their work.

   _____

Imagine that you are an animal. What quality do you have that would make you helpful to people?

Offender Gets a Second Chance

"I was one of the lucky ones," said Dan. "I was in a cell for six days instead of three months. However, that was six days too long!"

Dan committed a crime. Because Dan was under 18 years of age and his crime was minor, he was assigned to a community service program. The program was full, so Dan was made an alternate and sent to Juvenile Hall to wait for an opening in the program. Dan joined seven other young offenders in a cell at Juvenile Hall. "The cell was made of concrete and steel," Dan explained. "It wasn't locked, but we weren't allowed to leave it for more than 15 minutes each hour."

After six dismal days in the cell, Dan and his cellmates were told there was room for them in the community service program. The program required Dan to perform 300 hours of community service. Dan's community service jobs ranged from helping a mechanic at the city garage to picking up litter along the highway.

"It wasn't too bad," Dan said after completing his 300 hours. "I had to work hard. Whenever I wasn't at work or school, I had to stay home. My counselor made unexpected visits to my home. I could have been sent back to Juvenile Hall if I hadn't been home when I was supposed to be."

"Sometimes these teenagers think they're getting off easy for their offenses," said Tammy Tate, Dan's supervisor in the program. "We quickly show them they'll have to work hard. We're quick to zero in on those who goof off. We'll give one warning. If a teen continues to goof off, he's sent back to Juvenile Hall. There's always an alternate waiting to join the community service program in his place. These teens have a choice. They either work or go back to Juvenile Hall."

Last year, 165 juveniles participated in the community service program. They performed 3,852 hours of service to the community.

"The program is having positive results," said Judge Carey, the program's developer. "Our community is benefiting from the service, and the teenagers involved are benefiting from the employment. The program has even had a positive effect on troubled teenagers. They've shown an improvement in their attitudes by the time they've finished the program," said the judge.

"These teenagers are also gaining valuable employment experience," added Tammy Tate. "They're working in a variety of settings. This will give them skills which will help them secure employment later in life."

"This program offered me a chance to work toward the good of the community," said Dan. "I really felt good about doing something worthwhile. I've also learned a lot of skills in the jobs I've done. I liked the work I did for the mechanic in the city garage. I think I'll take an auto mechanics class in high school. Then, when I graduate, I can go to college and study to be a mechanic. Before I joined the community service program, my future looked dismal. Now I have a goal. I know I'll never spend time in a concrete cell again!"

"We've given troubled teens a reason to respect themselves and the community," said Judge Carey. People who respect themselves and their community are less likely to commit crimes."

Think It Over

Choose the best answer to complete each of the sentences below. Circle the letter of your choice.

1. Dan felt lucky because he _____.
   a. only spent six days in Juvenile Hall
   b. wasn't caught when he committed a crime
   c. didn't have to spend any time in a cell
   d. didn't have to work hard in the program

2. While in the community service program, Dan _____.
   a. performed 300 hours of community service
   b. helped a mechanic at the city garage
   c. picked up litter on the highway
   d. all of the above

3. A teen who goofs off in the program _____.
   a. is given three chances to straighten up
   b. is sent to jail
   c. is given one warning
   d. is sent home with a counselor

4. Last year, _____ juveniles participated in the community service program.
   a. 3,852
   b. 165
   c. 156
   d. 385

5. The main reason for writing this story was to tell readers about _____.
   a. the construction of the cells in Juvenile Hall
   b. the community service program
   c. Dan's future in Juvenile Hall
   d. Judge Carey's theory about troubled teens

Fill It In

Choose a word from the list below that belongs with each group of words.

alternate   cell   concrete   dismal   employment   goof

6. career, job, _____

7. cement, rock, _____

8. substitute, standby, _____

9. gloomy, miserable, _____

10. cage, jail, _____

Word Window

Read the words below. Circle the letters *ment* at the end of each word.

accomplishment   achievement   bewilderment   development

embarrassment   employment   measurement   settlement

Community Information

It is important for everyone, not just juvenile offenders, to respect his community. How much do you know about your community? Learn more about your community by visiting the library and answering these questions.

1. What city and state is your community in?

   _____

2. Who is the mayor of your city?

   _____

3. What is the population of your city?

   _____

4. Who is the governor of your state?

   _____

5. What services help people in your community?

   _____

6. What businesses help earn the money your community needs?

   _____

7. What makes your community different from other communities?

   _____

What service would you like to provide for the people in your community? Why?

"Central High School in Linn County will hold football tryouts August 12. For the first time in Central High history, girls are welcome," stated the announcement in the *Linn County Herald*.

"You may be welcome," said Marsha Butler to her daughter Rebecca, "but you won't be there! I've pondered the situation and made my decision. I forbid you to play football on a boys' team!"

Last fall, Rebecca Butler and her friend Erin Wise asked to try out for the boys' football team. Coach Jack Taylor was concerned about the matter. He met with Rebecca, Erin and ex-player Jenny Wheeler but was still unsure. So he referred the girls' request to the school board for a formal decision.

The school board debated the request throughout a very long session. They couldn't make a decision. Finally, they voted to table the request. They decided to study the matter and vote on it again before the next season's tryouts.

Last January, two physicians attended a school board session. Dr. Lee Chan described the injuries that are common on a football field. "I don't feel that the smaller female body is prepared for such rough physical treatment," said Dr. Chan. "I am against allowing the girls to join the football team."

"Dr. Chan should've brought facts instead of opinions," said Dr. Todd Wise. "Teenage girls aren't always smaller than teenage boys. Also, girls don't get injured more easily than boys. If the girls are willing to take the risk, it's not fair to forbid them!"

In March, a school board member took an opinion poll of the Linn County principals. According to the poll, most principals felt that the girls should've been allowed to try out for the football team.

The school board members discussed the poll in their May session. Kendra Hawkins, the school board's attorney, was present. "A school board in Kentucky was sued because they made a formal policy forbidding girls to try out for boys' teams," said Ms. Hawkins. "If we make such a policy, we could be sued. I've pondered the matter. I feel that no such formal policy should be made."

A special session of the school board was held in July. Parents were asked to attend. "Your sons and daughters are all invited to try out for the football team in August," announced school board president Karen Peck. "The exact date will be listed in the *Linn County Herald*."

"I forbid Rebecca to go through with this. I don't want her hurt," said Marsha Butler after Ms. Peck's announcement. "Rebecca is a mature girl. Most of the time I allow her to make her own decisions. However, it's just too hazardous for girls on the football field! I can't allow her to do this! I can't believe the school board would allow her to put herself in such a dangerous situation! They should've been thinking about our children instead of worrying about being sued!"

"Football is no more dangerous for girls than it is for boys," answered Dr. Todd Wise. "I'm going to let my daughter Erin make her own decision. I can understand your concern for your daughter. I'm as concerned as you are. However, you should understand that it's not fair for the school board to forbid all girls to try out."

"I'm glad we've had time to ponder this matter," said Coach Jack Taylor. "I'm still not sure how I feel about coaching girls on the football team. If many parents agree with Mrs. Butler, I won't find out this season!"

Think It Over

Choose the best answer to complete each sentence below. Circle the letter of each answer.

1. Coach Taylor referred the girls' request to the school board because _____.
   a. he didn't want to be sued
   b. he was unsure about the request
   c. Karen Peck asked him to
   d. all tryout requests are referred to the school board

2. The first time the school board members discussed the girls' request, they decided to _____.
   a. make a formal policy about tryouts
   b. let the girls try out
   c. table the matter and study it
   d. invite an attorney to join the discussion

3. The two physicians who advised the school board _____.
   a. agreed that girls shouldn't play football
   b. agreed that girls should play football
   c. agreed that girls are smaller than boys
   d. none of the above

4. A school board in Kentucky was sued because _____.
   a. a girl was injured on the football field
   b. they forbid girls to try out for football
   c. they allowed girls to play football
   d. they lied in an opinion poll

5. Another title for this article could be _____.
   a. Mom Forbids Football
   b. Linn County School Board Sued
   c. Ex-player Helps Develop Formal Policy
   d. Doctor's Agree at Meeting

Fill It In

Choose the best vocabulary word from the list to complete each sentence below.

forbid   formal   poll   pondered   session   should've

6. The party is _____, so please wear a suit and tie.

7. I knew I _____ brought my umbrella. I'm soaking wet!

8. I _____ the question all night, but I still don't know the answer.

9. According to the pre-election _____, most people would vote no.

10. "Order! Order! Court is in _____."

Word Window

Read each contraction below. Circle the letters 've at the end of each word. What word do these letters stand for?

could've   I've   should've   they've
we've   who've   would've   you've

Football Facts

In the story, Dr. Wise said that Dr. Chan should've used facts instead of opinions. It's not always easy to tell the two apart. See how well you do! Write a letter *F* in front of each fact and a letter *O* in front of each opinion.

_____ 1. Girls should not play football.

_____ 2. Few girls play on high school football teams.

_____ 3. Some girls are smaller than boys.

_____ 4. Girls are too small to be on a dangerous football field.

_____ 5. The school board should not make a formal policy.

_____ 6. Kendra Hawkins said that the school board shouldn't make a formal policy.

_____ 7. Football is no more dangerous for girls than it is for boys.

_____ 8. Some players have been seriously injured on football fields.

_____ 9. According to a poll, principals felt that girls should be allowed to try out.

_____ 10. It's not fair to forbid girls to try out for football.

Should people use facts or opinions to make decisions? Why?

Drugs Change Student's Future

Ted was a "straight A" student studying political science in college. He came from an honorable family that was proud of him. Ted had dreams of becoming an attorney, and it looked like those dreams would come true. But suddenly, Ted found himself staring at the walls of a dismal jail cell, wondering how he had become entangled in the ordeal that changed his life.

"I'm so depressed and confused," declared Ted. "I feel like I've thrown away my chance for an honorable future! How could I have become entangled in drug dealing?

"It started with my friend Conner," Ted remembered. "He'd heard that drugs were easy to buy on a college campus, and he pressured me to buy some for him. I told him that I scorned the use of drugs and wouldn't get involved.

"I forgot about that discussion with Conner until a month later," added Ted. "I was studying for a political science test with my classmate Peg. Peg and I had been studying for hours and were exhausted. Peg offered me some drugs to keep me going. Again, I said that I scorned the use of drugs. Peg left, but she told me to let her know if I ever changed my mind about the drugs.

"Later the same evening, Conner showed up at my door," Ted continued. "He looked terrible! 'You've got to help me,' he said. 'I need some drugs. I've promised them to an important buyer. If I don't supply the drugs, the result will be unbearable! I'll split the profit with you and we'll both be rich!' I ponder the situation now, and I don't know why I listened to him. I just couldn't muster enough courage to resist so much pressure from a friend! I made the biggest mistake in my life and called Peg. I didn't think about the consequences of becoming entangled in a drug deal. I didn't think about how horrified my family would be. I just didn't think at all. That's when this ordeal began.

"Peg hurried over to deliver the drugs," remembered Ted. "Conner begged me to accompany him to make the deal. We sold the drugs to a middle-aged man, who gave us a large amount of money. As we were leaving, another man stopped us. We soon discovered that the buyer and his partner were agents for the Federal Bureau of Investigation."

Ted pondered his situation before he continued. "Now I'm facing five years in prison. I feel terrible for my family. They've been helpful and understanding, but I know this has been a shock to them. I wish I'd thought about the consequences before I put my family through such an unbearable ordeal!

"I think a lot about the career that will never be mine," Ted said. "I wanted to be an attorney. I wanted to put people in jail for dealing drugs, but now I'm on the other side. I've made the biggest mistake of my life, and now I have to pay the consequences. I've learned how dangerous it is to get involved with drugs. Actually, I'm lucky that I only lost my dream. Many people who become involved with drugs lose their lives. I'd like to warn other students to think about the effects of their actions before becoming entangled with drugs. I'd like to tell them to scorn any involvement with drugs no matter how much pressure they get from friends!

"I was expelled from the university as soon as the dean heard about my ordeal. However, I plan to enroll in the educational program in prison. If I study hard, I can earn my college degree during my five years in jail. Maybe, if I work hard enough, I can still go to law school someday. My criminal record will change my dream of putting drug dealers in jail. However, I will qualify for some legal careers. It will be hard, but I hope I can put this ordeal behind me. I hope I can make my life honorable again. I know I'm going to try."

53

Think It Over

Choose the answer that best completes each sentence below. Circle the letter of each correct answer.

1. The biggest mistake of Ted's life was _____.
   a. becoming Conner's friend
   b. dropping out of college
   c. getting entangled in a drug deal
   d. not studying for his political science test

2. Ted's ordeal began when _____.
   a. he met Connor in elementary school
   b. he called Peg to ask for drugs
   c. he forgot to study for his test
   d. he graduated from law school

3. In the story, the middle-aged men were _____.
   a. Ted's political science professors
   b. the attorneys hired by Ted's parents
   c. drug dealers
   d. Federal Bureau of Investigation agents

4. Ted's family _____.
   a. is very honorable
   b. has been through an unbearable ordeal
   c. has been helpful and understanding
   d. all of the above

5. Ted wanted to use this story to _____.
   a. warn students to scorn any involvement with drugs
   b. beg the judge to let him out of jail
   c. convince his professors to send his class work to jail
   d. warn students to study for all their tests

Fill It In

Choose the best vocabulary word from the list to fill in each blank in the story.

entangled   honorable   ordeal   political   scorned   unbearable

Brian had always been an honest and 6. _____ person, until the

election. He wanted to win! He wanted a 7. _____ career. He

wanted it so much that he cheated to win the election. He was soon 8. _____

by everyone who learned that he'd cheated. He was thrown out of the election.

The 9. _____ was 10. _____ to Brian.

He decided never to cheat again!

Word Window

Circle the suffix -able in each of the words below. Read the words and use them in sentences.

agreeable   considerable   dependable   enjoyable
favorable   honorable   noticeable   respectable

Peer Pressure

Ted made a bad choice because he listened to his friend instead of thinking about the consequences of his choice. Read the story below. Think about the choices that Tammy could make. Then, answer the questions.

Tammy is babysitting the Jorgensen children. The Jorgensens asked her not to have any friends visit her while she was in their home. Tammy promised them no one would visit. Shortly after Mr. and Mrs. Jorgensen left, four of Tammy's friends knocked on the door. They wanted to come in and listen to music on the Jorgensen's new stereo and look for some food.

What could happen if Tammy lets her friends in the Jorgensen's house?

_____

_____

_____

What could happen if she doesn't let them in?

_____

_____

_____

What do you think Tammy should do? Why?

_____

_____

_____

Why is it important to think about the consequences before making an important decision?

Applying for a Summer Job

You've just heard about the perfect summer job. It's close to your house. It pays well. But most important, the job is in your favorite place in the whole world — the amusement park! The amusement park needs someone to work on the water slide! Your dream job is waiting for you!

You can't wait to apply for the job. It's vital to your happiness to get this job. You rush into your room to get dressed. You know that it's hot in the amusement park, so you decide to wear your cool, comfortable old shorts and your favorite thongs. After you dress, you rush outside, hop on your trusty bike and heartily pedal to the amusement park.

As the wind rushes through your hair and the scenery races by, you plan your wonderful summer working at the amusement park. Suddenly, you're there! You park your bike and look for a comb. You realize that you've left your comb at home, so you pat your hair with your sweaty hands.

Twenty minutes later, you walk slowly back to your bike. You didn't get the job. On top of everything else, you lost one of your thongs! It hasn't been a good day.

You decide to stop at your best friend's house on the way home. Her mom is an employment counselor at a job-finding service. Maybe she can tell you what you did wrong.

"Attitude and appearance are the two things employers look for most in an employee," says Mrs. Carlson. "There is nothing more vital to bring in when applying for employment than a positive attitude. One of the best ways for a person to show the right attitude is through a tidy appearance."

"What were you wearing when you applied?" asks your best friend Maria.

You step in front of a mirror and notice the spots on your shorts, your wrinkled, untucked shirt, your one thong and your messy hair.

"Oh, nothing special," you answer. "Maria, your mom's a genius! I can still get my dream job!"

You heartily thank Mrs. Carlson for her help and rush home. An hour later, you're standing in front of the amusement park again. This time you look quite tidy in dress clothes, nice shoes and freshly combed hair. You feel like a genius as you confidently walk through the door to the office.

"This morning, a young person walked in here with a wrinkled T-shirt, dirty shorts and thongs," says Mr. Edwards, the owner of the amusement park. "This person could've been a genius but didn't have an appearance that communicated a positive attitude. A successful business is built on the positive attitudes of the people it employs. You certainly look neat and tidy compared to other job-seekers! I bet you have a positive attitude! Why don't we talk about this job?"

You realize that Mr. Edwards doesn't recognize you from this morning. What a difference a tidy appearance has made! You've learned an important lesson. It's vital to have a positive attitude and a tidy appearance when applying for a job. You've become a job-seeking genius!

56

Think It Over

Choose the best answer to complete each sentence below. Circle the letter of each correct answer.

1. In the story, Mrs. Carlson is _____.
   a. your best friend's mom
   b. a counselor at a job-finding service
   c. the owner of the amusement park
   d. both a and b

2. The two things employers look for most in an employee are _____.
   a. genius and intelligence
   b. attitude and appearance
   c. appearance and intelligence
   d. attitude and intelligence

3. In the story when you looked in the mirror, you saw _____.
   a. a wrinkled shirt
   b. a pair of thongs
   c. jeans
   d. your friend

4. Mr. Edwards is _____.
   a. a job-finding counselor
   b. your best friend's dad
   c. looking for a genius
   d. the owner of an amusement park

5. Another title for this story could be _____.
   a. Counselors Vital to Job-Seekers
   b. Are You a Genius? If So, Please Apply
   c. Attitude and Appearance Are Vital to Job-Seekers
   d. Edwards Buys Amusement Park

Fill It In

Choose the best vocabulary word from the list to fill in each blank in the sentences.

amusement   genius   heartily   thongs   tidy   vital

6. *Hands* are to *gloves* as *feet* are to _____.

7. *Dark* is to *light* as *messy* is to _____.

8. *Big* is to *enormous* as *important* is to _____.

9. *Crying* is to *sadness* as *laughing* is to _____.

10. *Sports* is to *athlete* as *studying* is to _____.

Word Window

Read the words below. Circle the suffix -*ly* in each word. Think of a sentence to use each word.

admiringly	contentedly	doggedly	heartily
longingly	miserably	questioningly	wobbly

Dress for Success

You've learned it is appropriate to have a tidy appearance when applying for a job. Different appearances are appropriate for different activities. Read the activities below and describe the appropriate appearances.

1. riding a horse in a rodeo

   _____

2. playing football

   _____

3. scuba diving

   _____

4. getting married

   _____

5. giving a large dog a bath

   _____

6. going to a costume party

   _____

7. working in a hospital

   _____

8. eating dinner at a formal restaurant

   _____

What is your current appearance appropriate for?

K-9 Unit Goes to Court

"I've been an attorney with the police department for 10 years," said Charles Litow. "I've spoken on behalf of many fine police officers. Now, I'm learning to speak on behalf of police dogs as well!

"During the past three months, seven lawsuits have been filed against the K-9 Unit," added Mr. Litow.

"These lawsuits are interesting," said Police Chief Herrera. "There are many attorneys in this city. Yet, only one attorney has filed suits against the K-9 Unit. It seems strange that all seven individuals would choose the same attorney. I suspect this money-hungry attorney labeled our dogs bloodthirsty, and then went looking for victims."

"I'm just trying to prevent an injustice," said attorney Fred Morton, who spoke on behalf of suspects bitten by police dogs. "These dogs are bloodthirsty. They shouldn't be allowed to attack people. I understand the K-9 Unit can be useful, but the police officers aren't controlling the bloodthirsty animals.

"Sergeant Jim West is an example of an officer who didn't control his dog," explained Mr. Morton. "He warned Eric Harris that a K-9 Unit dog would search his home. Regulations state that an officer must wait 30 seconds after the warning before unleashing a search dog. However, Mr. Harris claims West only waited a few seconds before unleashing the animal. It was Mr. Harris's misfortune that Sergeant West didn't follow the rules."

"I know I waited the full 30 seconds," said Jim West. "I'm always very careful to follow the rules. I know my dog can be vicious. I only release him when it's necessary. I always give a warning first, and then wait the full 30 seconds before releasing him."

"There were three officers with Jim West," said Judge Howard Shipley. "I've studied their reports of this incident. According to all the reports, Sergeant West waited the

full 30 seconds before he unleashed the dog. I've also talked to the suspect, Eric Harris. Mr. Harris admitted he wasn't sober during the incident. I don't believe he was sober enough to realize 30 seconds passed between the warning and the release of the dog. I believe Sergeant West correctly followed regulations. I don't believe this was a case of injustice."

"Some individuals have been attacked by our dogs," said Police Chief Herrera. "However, they were attacked at appropriate times. Some of them refused to leave their hideouts after being warned that a search dog would be used. Other suspects tried to escape or attack a police officer. We've investigated all of the claims. We've found no evidence of injustice. My officers perform their duties well and according to regulations. Our dogs can be vicious, but they are obedient and properly controlled.

"It is a misfortune that these charges may give the K-9 Unit a bad name. We think the charges are an injustice to the fine work our officers are doing. However, there may be one positive effect from this publicity. People are more aware police dogs will attack upon command. More suspects may leave their hideouts to avoid an attack by the dogs. That would make arrests of suspects safer and quicker."

Think It Over

Circle the letter of the best answer to complete each sentence below.

1. During the past three months, _____.
   a. police dogs bit more suspects
   b. police dogs were locked up
   c. seven lawsuits were filed against the K-9 Unit
   d. seven crimes were committed

2. The seven suspects who sued the K-9 Unit _____.
   a. refused to leave their hideouts
   b. chose the same attorney
   c. waited 30 seconds before calling their attorney
   d. were bitten by the same dog

3. Eric Harris may not have realized 30 seconds passed before the dog's release because _____.
   a. he wasn't sober
   b. he didn't have a watch
   c. he didn't hear the warning
   d. he didn't see the dog

4. According to Chief Herrera, a dog might attack if the suspect _____.
   a. leaves his hideout when asked
   b. attacks a police officer
   c. tries to escape
   d. both b and c

5. A positive effect from this story was making people aware _____.
   a. the K-9 Unit has a bad name
   b. there are many attorneys in the city
   c. police dogs will attack
   d. many suspects have hideouts

Fill It In

Choose the best vocabulary word from the list to complete each sentence below.

behalf   bloodthirsty   hideouts   injustice   misfortune   sober

6. According to many stories, vampires are _____.

7. I knew I'd win the debate if Tony argued on my _____.

8. It was difficult for the police to find the suspect because he had many

   _____.

9. "I don't deserve to be grounded! This is such an _____!"

10. Last summer's drought was a _____ for many farmers.

Word Window

Read the words below. What two words make up the compound words?

bloodthirsty   hideout   rainstorm   stagecoach
toothpaste   wildflower   wintertime   wristwatch

You Be the Judge

In the story, Judge Howard Shipley listened to both sides of the story to decide which person was right. Now, it's your turn to be the judge.

Read the two versions of this story to decide who is right. Next, explain your decision on the lines below. Be sure to tell both people how to solve their problem.

"I was in my own backyard," said Brad. "Renee's vicious dog jumped the fence and attacked me. Her fence should have been taller to keep her bloodthirsty dog in its own yard. Actually, she shouldn't even own such a vicious dog!"

"P.J. isn't a vicious dog," answered Renee. "He's never bitten anyone before. I saw Brad teasing him before he jumped over the fence. He threw rocks at P.J. and squirted him with the hose. P.J. wouldn't jump over the fence unless he was teased! Brad should learn to treat animals nicely!"

_____

_____

_____

_____

_____

_____

_____

What breed of dog might P.J. be? What makes you think so?

The Money Counselor

The Money Counselor responds to readers' money questions in a weekly newspaper column. He hopes these letters answer your money questions.

---- ❖ ----

Dear Money Counselor:

All of my friends are employed. They always have enough money to go to movies and amusement parks, and eat out at restaurants. I'm not quite old enough to have a job. I have to request a loan from my parents whenever I want to go anywhere with my friends. Then, I have to listen to my parents lecture me about my rowdy friends. What an insult!

In a few months, I'll turn 16 and I'll be old enough to find employment. However, I don't know if I can keep my temper until then! What can I do to erase this unbearable problem?

Rowdy Rob

---- ❖ ----

Dear Rowdy Rob,

First, you need to understand that there's no way to erase any problem. However, most problems can be solved and I'll try to assist in solving yours.

You should explain your feelings to your parents. I'm sure they'll understand how you feel about requesting a loan. Try to work with your parents to institute a plan. Offer to do household chores and politely ask to be paid a fair amount for the work that you do. It's important for you to understand that your parents aren't trying to insult you. They have your best interests at heart.

Finally, you need to remember that losing your temper can be expensive! Patience, however, can be rewarding!

The Money Counselor

Dear Money Counselor:

My parents presented me with a credit card on my sixteenth birthday. Unfortunately I wasn't a responsible credit card user. I charged often and soon found that I couldn't make the minimum payments. My credit card was canceled. It was embarrassing, but I learned an important lesson. I also earned a bad credit rating.

My problem is I can't erase my bad credit rating. I'm trying to get a loan to buy a used car, but no one will lend money to a person with a bad credit rating. If I can't get a car, I may lose my job. I'm older now and more responsible. I believe I deserve another chance. How long will it be before I can erase my bad credit history?

Older and Wiser

---- ❖ ----

Dear Older and Wiser,

Destroying a good credit rating requires very little effort. Erasing a bad credit rating, however, takes much time and effort.

Some banks will institute an account to help people like you. It allows people to regain their good credit rating. To participate, you'll be required to deposit money into a savings account. Then, you'll be issued a credit card with a charge limit equal to the deposit. If you make your payments on time, you'll erase your bad credit rating. If you don't, the deposit in the savings account will be used to make the payment. Then, the credit card will be canceled and your credit rating will be more dismal than before.

The Money Counselor

Think It Over

Circle the letter of the best answer to complete each sentence below.

1. How old was Rowdy Rob when he wrote his letter?
   a. 15
   b. 16
   c. 18
   d. 21

2. Rowdy Rob felt insulted when _____.
   a. his friends asked for money
   b. his friends teased him about not having a job
   c. his parents lectured him about his friends
   d. he read the Money Counselor's letter

3. Older and Wiser was embarrassed when _____.
   a. he had to buy a used car
   b. his credit card was canceled
   c. his parents gave him a credit card
   d. he had to use his parents' credit card

4. Older and Wiser needs a loan to _____.
   a. buy a house
   b. make credit card payments
   c. go to college
   d. buy a used car

5. The Money Counselor column _____.
   a. answers the readers' money questions
   b. can be found every week
   c. is in the Business News section of the newspaper
   d. all of the above

Fill It In

Choose the correct word from the list to fill in each sentence below.

erase   institute   insult   loan   rowdy   temper

6. *Do* is to *undo* as *write* is to _____.

7. *Happiness* is to *sadness* as *compliment* is to _____.

8. *Food* is to *restaurant* as _____ is to *bank*.

9. *Quiet* is to *loud* as *calm* is to _____.

10. *Stop* is to *start* as *cancel* is to _____.

Word Window

Wow! You've completed another 10 lessons! Read the following words from Lessons 11 through 19.

review	championship	favorable
reassure (11)	friendship (14)	respectable (17)
confidence	achievement	wobbly
conference (12)	bewilderment (15)	doggedly (18)
ex-president	I've	rainstorm
ex-firefighter (13)	you've (16)	wildflower (19)

Money Talks

Someday, you may have a chance to give advice about money. You will give better advice if you use money words properly. Match the words below to their definition. Write the word on the line beside the definition. You may use a dictionary to help you.

debtor	asset	debt	interest
coinage	bankroll	income	creditor

1. An _____ is something owned, a resource.

2. A _____ is a supply of money.

3. _____ is the process of making coins.

4. A _____ is someone you owe money to.

5. A _____ is something you owe to someone.

6. A _____ is someone who owes you something.

7. _____ is money earned from work.

8. _____ is a charge for borrowing money or a reward for saving money.

Would you rather be a debtor or a creditor? Why?

64

A Healthy Business

What's your medical problem — a toothache, a sunburn or a blister? If your problem's not serious, a remedy may be closer than your doctor's office. You can probably solve your problem with a home medical kit.

While the American public may not follow healthy practices, the home medical kit market is very healthy. Annual sales are in the hundreds of millions of dollars. Business has boomed in recent years and is expected to continue.

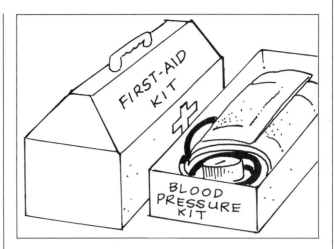

Many specialized kits are available. Their prices range from one dollar to several hundred dollars. You can buy a home medical kit to examine your eyes, ears, nose and throat. You can use another kit to interpret the sound from your heart and lungs. You can test for high blood pressure with the help of yet another home medical kit. You can also buy kits with specialized treatments for poisoning and burns. You can even find a home medical kit to mix the materials for a temporary tooth filling.

"The home medical kit market has boomed during the last few years," says Dr. Austin Mills. "This boom is the result of many factors. One factor is the rising cost of medical visits. It has become more expensive for doctors to practice medicine. They have no choice but to pass the rising costs to patients. Many people can't afford to see a doctor for every medical problem. Home medical kits offer an alternate source of health care.

"Another factor is a movement toward self-care," adds Dr. Mills. "People are becoming more responsible for their own health care. A home medical kit can help people take better care of themselves.

"The third factor is definitely a major one," explains Dr. Mills. "Companies that make home medical kits are using effective advertising and marketing strategies to boost sales. These strategies convince customers that a home medical kit can be a safe, easy and inexpensive remedy for a health problem.

"I personally have mixed feelings about home medical kits," admits Dr. Mills. "I ask myself how reliable these kits are? Some kits have been tested and seem to be very reliable. The fact is that the kit is as reliable as the person using it. That person needs to interpret and follow the directions accurately. If he doesn't, the kit can do more harm than good.

"Some medical problems are serious," warns Dr. Mills. "If people aren't properly treated by a doctor, it could be a fatal mistake. People with serious conditions could incorrectly interpret the results from a home medical kit. They could try to help themselves with a treatment that's actually dangerous. It's safest for people to rely on home medical kits in addition to seeing a doctor, not instead of a doctor.

"I would advise patients with a blister or sunburn to look for a reliable home remedy," says Dr. Mills. "However, people with serious medical problems should see their doctors. It can be quite dangerous for some patients to play doctor!"

Think It Over

Choose the best answer to complete each sentence below. Circle the letter of each correct answer.

1. According to Dr. Mills, home medical kits are popular because _____.
   a. visits to the doctor's office are more expensive
   b. people are more responsible for their health care
   c. companies effectively advertise their kits
   d. all of the above

2. Advertising convinces customers that home medical kits are _____.
   a. safe and easy
   b. safe and expensive
   c. safe and difficult
   d. reliable and expensive

3. Dr. Mills feels that home a medical kit is _____.
   a. always dangerous to use
   b. always reliable, especially with serious medical problems
   c. as reliable as the person using it
   d. better than doctor visits

4. Patients with _____ should use home remedies.
   a. broken legs
   b. sunburns
   c. serious heart conditions
   d. serious infections

5. The main idea of this story is home medical kits _____.
   a. are always dangerous according to most doctors
   b. are helpful to people who don't have serious medical problems
   c. are forcing doctors to charge more for office visits
   d. are for everybody

Fill It In

Choose the best word from the list to fill in each blank in the story.

blister   interpret   reliable   remedy   specialized   sunburn

Last weekend, I fell asleep next to the pool. I slept in the sun for three hours. When I awoke,

I had a terrible 6. _____! I saw a huge 7. _____

on my arm! I rushed to the drugstore for a 8. _____. Mrs. Horton

suggested a 9. _____ cream to heal sunburn. She said it was very

10. _____ and always worked for her. I tried the cream and felt better

instantly. I'll never sleep in the sun again!

Word Window

Read each word below. Circle the letters *ize* in each word. Think about the meanings of the words.

apologize   civilize   energize   familiarize

legalize   specialize   sympathize   terrorize

Medical Advice

You have a job in a drugstore. People ask for medical advice all day. Read the problems below. Write your advice on the lines under each problem. If the problem is serious, advise the person to see a doctor. If the problem isn't serious, write what items belong in that home medical kit.

1. a sunburn _____

_____

2. a minor cold _____

_____

3. ear infection _____

_____

4. a broken arm _____

_____

5. a paper cut _____

_____

Would you rather be a doctor or work in a drugstore? Why?

67

The Psychology of Losing

It was game time. The fans were ready for the action to begin. The Northridge Mustangs ran onto the court while their fans cheered loudly. The cheers stopped when the home team ran onto the court followed by their coach, Delbert Brown. The Twin Town Tigers heard hostile boos and disgusted jeering from their side of the bleachers.

"These tough times bring out the ugly side of sports," said Coach Brown. "It's unfortunate and disgusting that these high school kids have to listen to the hostile jeers. I wish the fans would realize it's easier for the players to win when they aren't insulted by their own fans."

"It's very discouraging," said Pat Sanders, a player for the Tigers. "Last year we always had the support of our cheering fans. Some male fans decided not to shave until we lost a game. Many of them had very long beards last year. Unfortunately, there are no beards this year."

"Last year, our rival teams were insulted. This year, it's us," agreed teammate Enrico Hernandez. "I know we're not doing as well as last year, but it's hard when the fans jeer their home team."

Many members of the Twin Town Tigers share these feelings. They are limping through the season with a record of six losses and no wins. It's a tough season for the team. The disgusted jeers from the hostile fans make it worse. Coach Brown decided to ask a sports psychology expert to help his team.

"I know the jeers are hard to bear," Dr. Earl Satir, specialist in sports psychology told the team. "However, you need to understand why the fans are jeering. This season is frustrating for the fans as well as for you. You have the chance to play against rival teams. The action on the court helps you manage your frustration. Your fans can't jump on the court and play, so they have to handle their feelings in other ways.

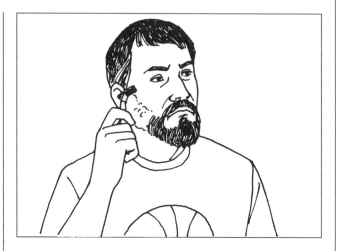

"People handle frustration in three ways," explained Dr. Satir to the team. "Some people get depressed. These people stop coming to games or leave at halftime. If you've noticed fewer people at your games, it's because this type of fan has stopped attending.

"Other people use humor to handle their feelings. These people make jokes about the team, but they don't get hostile. There may even be people like this on your team.

"The third type of people don't release their frustrations through humor," added Dr. Satir. "They're more likely to be verbal attackers. They release their frustrations by verbally yelling or attacking those they feel are responsible. The attackers target their hostile remarks at the coach, the players or the officials. These are the people that you hear jeering and booing."

"What can we do to stop the jeering?" asked Pat.

"I'm afraid you can't stop it," said Dr. Satir. "Hopefully, now that you understand the hostile fans, the jeers may not bother you as much. Just concentrate on the game and ignore the attackers. I have faith that you'll begin winning games. Please remember, though, the most important thing is to have fun and to do your best. Don't play for the spectators. Play for yourselves. If you do that, you'll always be winners."

Think It Over

Choose the best answer to complete each sentence below.   Circle the letter of each correct answer.

1. The _____ were cheered as they ran onto the court.
   a. Twin Town Tigers
   b. officials for the game
   c. Northridge Mustangs
   d. Twin Town marching band

2. The Twin Town fans grew long beards when _____.
   a. the team was losing many games
   b. the team was winning many games
   c. the cost of shaving increased
   d. long beards were in style

3. It's harder for the fans to control their frustration because _____.
   a. the fans care more about winning
   b. the fans are attacked by the rival fans
   c. the fans can't jump on the court and play
   d. the fans don't have a psychology expert

4. Coach Brown asked a sports psychologist to _____.
   a. warn students not to jeer the team
   b. report the Tiger's season record
   c. explain to students why some fans jeer
   d. report the Tiger's had won a game

5. According to Dr. Satir, people handle frustration by _____.
   a. verbally attacking those they feel are responsible
   b. getting depressed
   c. making jokes
   d. all of the above

Fill It In

Choose the best word from the list below to fill in each sentence.

attackers   beard   disgusted   hostile   psychology   rival

6. *Head* is to *hair* as *chin* is to _____.

7. *Depressed* is to *happy* as *friendly* is to _____.

8. *Animals* are to *zoology* as *people* are to _____.

9. *Friend* is to *enemy* as *teammate* is to _____.

10. *Excited* is to *bored* as *pleased* is to _____.

Word Window

Read the words below. Circle the *-er* suffix in each word.

announcer   attacker   buyer   digger

dodger   publisher   picker   manufacturer

Why Did You Do That?

In the story, Earl Satir was a doctor of psychology. Psychologists explain people's behavior. Suppose you are a psychologist and can predict why people do things. Write your explanation for each situation below.

1. Why do people study?

   _____

   _____

2. Why do people play sports?

   _____

   _____

3. Why do people listen to music?

   _____

   _____

4. Why do people read?

   _____

   _____

5. Why do people cry?

   _____

   _____

Is it always easy to know why someone is doing something? Why? What things help you decide a person's mood?

Many Motorcycle Riders Unlicensed

"I was mad when the state trooper pulled me over," said Doug Lanning. "I didn't think I was doing anything wrong. Now I know that I was riding my motorcycle illegally. I didn't know that I needed a special motorcycle license. I thought my driver's license for my car was enough. I wasn't wearing a helmet either. That's how the state trooper noticed me.

"The day after I was pulled over, I went to my state's Driver's License Bureau and enrolled in a class for motorcycle safety," added Mr. Lanning. "I studied the *Biker's Safety Manual* and passed the skills test. Now, I am a licensed biker. I have learned to ride my motorcycle safely as well as legally. As I said, I was mad when the trooper pulled me over. Now, I'm glad he did. The $38 fine I paid was well worth all the safety knowledge I've gained."

"I wish we could make all bikers aware that it's vital for them to ride their motorcycles legally," said State Trooper Marcus Howard. "Too many riders are being injured in accidents. A publication by the State Traffic Safety Board shows that many riders who are injured don't have the correct license."

The State Traffic Safety Board publication included many facts. The publication states that 4,583 bikers were involved in accidents in the past two years. Only 1,742 of them had motorcycle riders' licenses. Therefore, only 38% of those bikers had enrolled in the safety class required to get the license.

According to the publication, bikers are likely to be seriously hurt in accidents. The two-year study showed that 80% of motorcycle accidents resulted in serious injury to the rider. Seven percent of these riders were killed.

"The number of injuries and deaths are much higher for people who drive motorcycles than they are for those who drive cars," said Trooper Howard. "That's why it's vital that bikers know they need more than a regular driver's license to ride a motorcycle. It's vital

that all bikers enroll in a motorcycle safety class, study the *Biker's Safety Manual* and pass the test for a motorcycle license. This is the only way for them to gain the experience they need to ride a motorcycle legally and safely. Inexperienced bikers are often injured or killed. These inexperienced bikers need to know that a motorcycle isn't a plaything. It can be quite dangerous if ridden illegally.

"It also worries me that 82% of the bikers killed in accidents last year weren't wearing helmets," added State Trooper Howard. "Helmets could have lowered this death toll."

"A motorcycle can be a fun way to travel. It's also less expensive than a car. However, when operated by an inexperienced rider without a helmet, a motorcycle is dangerous," said Gloria Edwards of the State Traffic Safety Board. "If you're a biker, there are things you can do to keep yourself from being counted in next year's death toll. First, you must understand that your motorcycle isn't a plaything. Second, enroll in a safety class. Study the manual and get your motorcycle license. Finally, always wear your helmet. This isn't just advice. It's the law. Breaking this law could also mean breaking your neck."

Think It Over

Choose the best answer to complete each sentence below. Circle the letter of each correct answer.

1. The day after he was pulled over, Doug Lanning _____.
   a. went to court to fight his ticket
   b. went to the police station to complain about the state trooper
   c. enrolled in a class for motorcycle safety
   d. sold his motorcycle

2. During a two-year period, _____ motorcycle riders were involved in accidents.
   a. 4,583
   b. 1,742
   c. 38%
   d. 80%

3. According to State Trooper Howard, it's vital that motorcycle riders _____.
   a. enroll in motorcycle safety classes
   b. study the *Biker's Safety Manual*
   c. pass the test for a special motorcycle rider's license
   d. all of the above

4. Gloria Edwards is _____.
   a. a state trooper
   b. a motorcycle rider who doesn't believe in helmets
   c. a part of the State Traffic Safety Board
   d. the author of the *Biker's Safety Manual*

5. This article was published to tell motorcycle riders that they should _____.
   a. have a regular automobile driver's license
   b. have a special motorcycle rider's license
   c. have their motorcycles fixed often so they're safe
   d. drive the speed limit at all times

Fill It In

Choose the word from the list below that belongs with each group of words.

enroll   inexperienced   manual   plaything   publication   toll

6. toy, game, amusement, _____

7. cost, expense, price, _____

8. register, sign up, join, _____

9. guidebook, textbook, handbook, _____

10. bulletin, newsletter, report, _____

Word Window

Read the words below. Circle the prefix *in-* in each word. Practice using the words in sentences.

inaccurate	inconvenient	incorrect	incredible
inexpensive	inexperienced	injustice	insane

Publication Percents

In many publications, such as the one by the State Traffic Safety Board, percents are used to report the facts. Remember that *percent* means *per hundred*. Then, figure out the percents for each fact below and write them on the lines provided. Finally, use the percents to write your own report.

1. 77 out of 100 people in Hometown have pets. _____ Percent

2. 32 out of 100 people in Hometown have cats. _____ Percent

3. 29 out of 100 people in Hometown have dogs. _____ Percent

4. 16 out of 100 people in Hometown have fish. _____ Percent

5. 15 out of 100 people in Hometown don't have pets, but want to get them. _____ Percent

6. 8 out of 100 people in Hometown don't like pets. _____ Percent

7. The national average for owning pets is 68 out of 100 people. _____ Percent

_____

_____

_____

_____

_____

_____

_____

_____

What do you think is the difference between your report and an actual publication?

Tip from Caller Helps Police

The Sheriff's Department received a helpful phone call from an unidentified caller yesterday. The caller reported a burglary. The tip helped officials recover stolen merchandise.

At 9:03 A.M., Police Officer Wilma Perkins received a call at the Sheriff's Communication Center. The caller said he believed there was a van traveling west on Highway 40 carrying stolen merchandise. He had overheard two men discussing the merchandise in a restaurant.

Officer Perkins radioed the information to officers on patrol. Fortunately, two officers were near the location the unidentified caller mentioned.

Within minutes, the officers had located and stopped the vehicle. It appeared to be loaded with stolen merchandise. A TV, some audio equipment and a briefcase of jewelry were found in the vehicle.

The police recovered the merchandise and completed the investigation by 9:47 A.M. The two men in the van were held for questioning. They faced arrest for receiving and concealing stolen merchandise.

At 9:53 A.M. Officer Perkins received a call from Mrs. John Taylor of Friends Drive. She said a burglary had occurred at her home after she left for work at 7:55 A.M. A neighbor had called her shortly after she'd arrived at work. The neighbor said she'd seen an unfamiliar van leaving the Taylor's driveway at 8:29 A.M. Mrs. Taylor rushed home to investigate. She was panicky when she found her home had been broken into.

Officer Perkins asked Mrs. Taylor to list any missing items. She reported their TV, some audio equipment and several pieces of her jewelry missing. She also indicated a briefcase might be missing.

Officer Perkins was surprised. Those were the same items the officers had found less than an hour ago. Mrs. Taylor's belongings had been recovered even before they were reported missing! Officer Perkins recommended Mrs. Taylor come to the Sheriff's Department immediately.

When Mrs. Taylor arrived, she identified the merchandise found in the van as her property.

Charges of first degree burglary were placed against the two drivers. Bond was set at $5,000 each. Their court appearance is scheduled for November 3.

Sheriff Wells said, "This incident demonstrates what can happen when the public cooperates to curb crime. This kind of public support and assistance can curb burglaries in our county."

Mrs. Taylor was pleased at the outcome. "I was panicky when my neighbor called and told me about the unfamiliar van leaving the driveway," she said. "I feel better now that the suspects can't raise the $5,000 bond and are in jail."

She hoped the police could identify the caller. She wanted to pay a reward of $100 in appreciation for the tip.

"I'm one of the lucky ones," she said. "Many homes are broken into every day. Some people never recover their belongings. My things were found before I even reported them missing. A good tip and effective police work deserve appreciation.

Think It Over

Circle the answer that best completes each item below.

1. Sheriff Wells says _____ can help curb crime.
   a. setting bond
   b. having public support
   c. identifying merchandise
   d. none of the above

2. Which happened last?
   a. Bond was set for the two suspects.
   b. Someone overheard the two suspects discussing the burglary.
   c. The merchandise was recovered.
   d. Mrs. Taylor's neighbor saw a strange van in the driveway.

3. Mrs. Taylor was panicky because _____.
   a. the two suspects were arrested
   b. her home had been broken into
   c. her TV had been stolen
   d. her merchandise had been reported missing

4. At 7:55 A.M. _____.
   a. a neighbor called Mrs. Taylor
   b. someone called the police station
   c. Mrs. Taylor left for work
   d. a van was seen in Mrs. Taylor's driveway

5. Another title for this story might be _____.
   a. Unidentified Caller Helps Police Solve Crime
   b. Reward Offered to Unidentified Caller
   c. Van Drivers Burglarize Home
   d. Two Burglary Suspects Thrown in Jail

Fill It In

Choose the correct vocabulary word from the list to complete each sentence below.

appreciation   audio   bond   burglarize   panicky   unidentified

6. Would you be _____ if your car ran out of gas?

7. An _____ friend sent me flowers.

8. The clerk at the record store is an _____ genius.

9. Mr. Pollen showed his _____ by taking us out to dinner.

10. The suspect posted _____ before he was released.

Word Window

Read each of the words below and tell what prefix is used. Explain the meaning of the prefix. Then, use some of the words in sentences.

unanswered	unidentified	undo	unpleasant
unaware	unbroken	unfit	unnecessary

Reap the Rewards

Mrs. Taylor found out the identity of the caller who reported the two suspects. Write a thank-you letter to that person on the lines below.

Dear _____,

_____

_____

_____

_____

Sincerely,

Mrs. John Taylor

Now, answer the questions below and share your answers with the rest of the class.

1. What does your family do to protect its home? _____

   _____

2. What are some things you've been told to keep yourself safe? _____

   _____

   _____

3. What activities in your neighborhood would you consider suspicious?

   _____

   _____

Under what circumstances would you call the police?

Man Wins Fight Against Polio

Health / Science

"Tom," the physician said, "the chance of you ever walking again is very slim."

Nine-year-old Thomas Butler heard those words as he lay in bed paralyzed with polio. The paralyzing attack started as a feverish feeling. After the fever, Thomas was very ill. Finally, he was unable to move his legs.

Today, 23 years later, Thomas is a firefighter. How he battled and finally defeated his handicap is a story of courage and inspiration. He recalls the agony and anguish he experienced. He felt like hiding in his bed for the rest of his life. But he knew he wanted a normal life again.

The depression was unbearable as he yearned to walk. There were nights of anguish when he was alone in his hospital bed. With determination, he struggled to move his paralyzed legs.

"At first, there was no movement at all," Thomas said. "I used to rub my legs to keep my muscles from tightening. I did exercises to strengthen my muscles to move like they used to. I did my exercises in a pool with other patients.

"Later," Thomas added, "the doctors put braces on my legs. The braces helped me stand, but it was approximately two months before I could take small steps. It was very painful, but I worked hard. Every day, I was able to walk a little farther.

"Soon, I had recovered enough so I could walk around the block. I asked my parents if I could have a newspaper route. For almost six months, I delivered a few papers in my neighborhood. The exercise was good for me. I was positive it would help me recover. My doctors agreed. They were amazed at my recovery. Then, I learned to ride my bike again, and I got a longer paper route."

Thomas told about his school years. "In seventh grade, I began to go to a gym where I did tumbling exercises and weight lifting. By

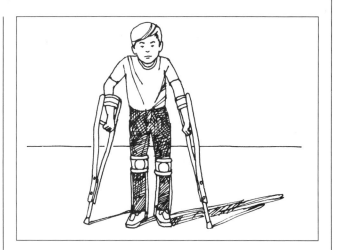

the time I was in eighth grade, I had recovered enough so the school let me join some sports teams."

Thomas acknowledges that he likes his firefighting job, but he yearns for his days off at this time of year. "During the eleventh grade," Thomas explained, I learned to ski. I hadn't recovered from the effects of the polio, but I yearned to get on the slopes. I certainly had my share of collisions. One ski season, I became a ski bum. I was a part-time employee, which gave me an opportunity to do lots of skiing. I know I skied more than I worked. During that season, I made many improvements and even won a few races."

Thomas has learned from his experiences. "I'm a volunteer in the children's ward at the community hospital," he said. "Some children have illnesses that make them feverish for weeks at a time. Others can't move their arms or legs. I acknowledge the fact that some of the children won't make great improvements.

"I wish I could become a full-time volunteer," he continued. "I know I could give some of the children the assistance and encouragement they need. If I could overcome my problems, so can they. Polio didn't stop me from achieving my goals. I want the children to know that they never have to give up their dreams."

Lesson 25   77

Think It Over

Circle the letter of the best answer for each item below.

1. Thomas Butler's battle to overcome his handicap is a story of _____.
   a. courage and inspiration
   b. agony and injustice
   c. tragedy and dismay
   d. sadness and pity

2. Which happened first? Thomas _____.
   a. joined a sports team
   b. became a volunteer
   c. became a firefighter
   d. delivered newspapers

3. Thomas would like to become a full-time volunteer because _____.
   a. he likes hospitals
   b. he wants to become a doctor
   c. he wants to encourage the children not to give up hope
   d. being a volunteer has been his dream

4. The doctors allowed Thomas to deliver papers because _____.
   a. they wanted papers delivered to the hospital
   b. the exercise would be good for Thomas
   c. Thomas would have to walk before he could ride a bike
   d. the walking exercise would help him become a ski bum

5. The main idea of this story is _____.
   a. Thomas had a disease when he was young
   b. many people with illnesses can lead normal lives
   c. walking is good exercise for polio victims
   d. Thomas has time to work, ski and be a volunteer

Fill It In

Choose the synonym or antonym from the list below to complete each sentence.

acknowledge   anguish   feverish   paralyzed   polio   yearned

6. *Joy* is an antonym of _____.

7. *Hot* is a synonym of _____.

8. _____ is an antonym of *dreaded*.

9. *Unable to move* means the same as _____.

10. _____ is an antonym of *ignore*.

Word Window

Each of the words below has the -ish suffix. Read each word and tell what it means.

childish   foolish   reddish   sheepish
feverish   pinkish   selfish   yellowish

Be a Volunteer!

Thomas was a volunteer in a hospital. People volunteer their time in many ways. The questions below will help you think more about volunteering.

1. Name some places where people can volunteer.

   _____

   _____

2. If you were a volunteer in a hospital, what job would you like to do? Why?

   _____

   _____

3. How could a hospital volunteer make a patient's stay less boring?

   _____

   _____

4. If you were a volunteer at a meal site, what job would you like to do? Why?

   _____

   _____

5. If you ate at a meal site, what would you like the volunteers to serve?

   _____

   _____

What do you think would be most rewarding about being a volunteer? Why?

Teens Fight Crime

Teens Against Crime is the name of a national organization to combat crime. Any teenager can join the program. The organization helps make neighborhoods safer. Several local chapters are already active. More are being developed.

Professor Kurt Maxey was appointed to organize Teens Against Crime. He took a leave of absence from his university to help with the group's formation. He's working temporarily in the Crime Prevention Bureau in the sheriff's department.

Professor Maxey explained, "We frequently hear about juvenile crime. It's true they commit their share of crimes. But teens are twice as often victims of serious crimes. They're the victims of adults and of each other. We want to change the image of teens as criminals. Most teens are law-abiding citizens.

"Teens Against Crime might be considered an extension of the Neighborhood Watch Program," he continued. "It involves teens who make communities safer."

Dr. Maxey assisted in the organization of the local chapters. However, the teens will soon take over as leaders.

Three students from Morris County were appointed to attend a national meeting. The meeting was held in Washington, D.C. Dwayne Carlson was one of the students who attended the meeting. He explained, "On the national level, the organization set three major goals. The first goal is for teens to avoid becoming victims. The second goal is for teens to know their community resources. The third goal stresses teamwork to make communities safer."

Teens were given an example of the goals. They learned how to identify a possible thief. Then, they learned which agency to call to report a thief. They worked together to decide the best ways to prevent thieves from stealing in their neighborhoods.

Juanita Lopez also attended the national meeting. She explained, "Students from each chapter attended the meeting. We worked together to set the national goals. But we also set goals for each chapter's community. Each community has its own problems."

Lopez said it was interesting to review each group's goals. Many groups addressed the drug problem. Some groups from big cities have a problem with subway crime. They attempted to find ways for teens to safely ride the subway.

"Teens Against Crime chapters are vital to safe communities," Dr. Maxey said. "Many teens are aware of criminal activities in their communities. They can often identify criminals before adults do. With the right training, teens can follow the proper procedures. They can play a big role in keeping their communities safer."

Teens interested in the formation of a Teens Against Crime chapter should contact Professor Maxey. His phone number at the Crime Prevention Bureau is 555-2000.

"Teens can make a difference," Dr. Maxey concluded. "They must take an active part in their communities. The absence of active teens means criminal activity will thrive. Offenders need to know the community won't allow crime, even temporarily. So just say 'yes' to Teens Against Crime."

Think It Over

Circle the letter of the best answer for each sentence below.

1. Chapter leaders of Teens Against Crime met in Washington, D.C., to decide _____.
   a. where to hold their next meeting
   b. national and community goals
   c. where to locate the national office
   d. how to recruit members

2. Professor Kurt Maxey has taken a leave of absence from his job to _____.
   a. attend a national meeting in Washington, D.C.
   b. identify major goals for the Teens Against Crime
   c. help organize Teens Against Crime
   d. work for the Crime Prevention Bureau

3. Teens Against Crime could be considered an extension of the Neighborhood Watch Program because _____.
   a. both want their goals to make neighborhoods safer
   b. Teens Against Crime works under the Neighborhood Watch Program
   c. the Neighborhood Watch Program provides funds to the chapters
   d. none of the above

4. One goal of Teens Against Crime is _____.
   a. to share experiences during a meeting
   b. to locate neighborhoods with the most crime
   c. to identify criminals in their neighborhoods
   d. to help teens avoid becoming victims

5. The main idea of this story is _____.
   a. organized and trained teens play a vital role in fighting crime
   b. Teens Against Crime replaces the Neighborhood Watch Program
   c. teens met in Washington, D.C., to set national goals
   d. teens are twice as likely as adults to be crime victims

Fill It In

Choose the best word from the list below to complete each sentence.

absence   appoint   chapter   formation   temporarily   subway

6. Would you like to join our newly formed youth _____?

7. Many people in large cities find it more convenient to ride the _____

   than to drive a car.

8. We hired a new manager in your _____.

9. The committee will _____ a new chairperson.

10. The _____ of a club takes time and energy.

Word Window

Look at the *-ation* ending in the words below. Read each word to yourself.

formation   foundation   starvation   publication
civilization   conversation   occupation   determination

Setting Goals

In this story, members of Teens Against Crime met to set national and community goals. Suppose you're a member of Teens Against Drugs. On the lines below, write your goals for the next year. Then, decide how to meet these goals. Which activities or groups will you sponsor?

Teens Against Drugs

Our chapter will:

_____

_____

_____

_____

_____

_____

To accomplish our goals, we will:

_____

_____

_____

_____

_____

_____

_____

Why is it important to set goals? What are some of your weekly or monthly goals?

82

Sheriff Wheeler Renews Pledge

Scott County Sheriff Frank Wheeler kicked off his reelection campaign bid Monday evening. He promised to bring new skills to his department if he's reelected. Wheeler spoke to almost 300 people attending the dinner.

"I feel we've made great strides during my first term," Wheeler said. "We can take pride in these strides. I want to repeat my first campaign pledge I made four years ago. I pledged to restore the principles of honesty and pride in the department. I kept my promise. The department has operated on these principles, not politics."

The *Daily Times* thinks Sheriff Wheeler has kept his promise. A recent newspaper editorial suggested he's been the most honest sheriff to hold this office in many years. The *Daily Times* said Wheeler was very concerned about the people who live in the county.

Wheeler successfully defeated Sheriff William Blake four years ago. County officials say Wheeler's good reputation hasn't been influenced by politics.

Wheeler said, "We can be proud of the highly qualified people we added to the department. These people have had many years of professional training. Two members of the force have trained at the National Deputies Training Academy. One of my goals is to continue hiring good workers. We'll hire many professionals. We'll send more deputies to the academy."

Wheeler moved on to a new topic. He said he obtained higher salaries for his workers. But he thinks even higher salaries are now needed to attract and keep highly qualified employees.

Then, Wheeler's tone turned more serious. He admitted some things could be improved. After taking office, Wheeler hired retired Agent Carl Brunson and former city Police Chief Kim Wolfe as assistants. They were criticized for several incidents. One incident

involved a deputy who some believe received unfair discipline from Agent Brunson and Ms. Wolfe. The deputy lost one week's wages for being late to work.

Wheeler acknowledged the incidents. "I agree the discipline was harsh. I've spoken with my assistants. I believe they understand how to handle such situations less harshly. The wages were returned to the deputy.

"We have other problems as well," Wheeler said. "While the editorial praised the job I'm doing, there are areas that need changes. The department has outdated radio equipment. Funds were approved to purchase the most modern equipment. The new radios should be here in a few weeks. They're the latest technology available. They will make you proud of our department."

Wheeler was asked to comment on his opponent. Ken Watson is a former police officer. Wheeler takes his opponent very seriously. He's promised a fair campaign.

"My opponent is challenging my bid for reelection. I'll run my campaign the way I run my department. I'll run on the principle of honesty. Honesty has brought pride to the department. The department will continue to have pride if I'm reelected to another term. May the best person win!"

Lesson 27

83

Think It Over

Circle the letter of the best answer for each sentence below.

1. Many officials believe Sheriff Wheeler is _____.
   a. seeking a higher salary
   b. harsh in disciplining employees
   c. very concerned about the people in the county
   d. very unpopular

2. One of Sheriff Wheeler's goals is to _____.
   a. continue hiring good workers
   b. cut back on the number of staff
   c. hire more women
   d. none of the above

3. According to Sheriff Wheeler, a deputy was unhappy because he _____.
   a. couldn't support the sheriff's opponent, Ken Watson
   b. didn't receive a higher salary
   c. wasn't appointed to attend the national training academy
   d. received unfair discipline

4. Sheriff Wheeler plans to _____.
   a. repair the existing radios
   b. replace the outdated radios
   c. remodel the offices and add computers
   d. wait for the budget to be approved and then add new radios

5. Sheriff Wheeler thinks his opponent, Ken Watson, _____.
   a. should not be taken seriously
   b. is someone to be taken seriously
   c. will not run a fair campaign
   d. can be easily beaten

Fill It In

Read the sentences below. Choose the best word from the list to complete each sentence.

academy   editorial   pledge   principles   reelection   term

6. Our country is run on the _____ of freedom and justice.

7. I plan to have a B average by the end of the school _____.

8. Ms. Lawson writes an _____ every other week.

9. Have you ever driven past the military _____?

10. The _____ campaign for mayor begins in April.

Word Window

The words in each pair below are pronounced the same.   Read the words to yourself and then aloud.

brakes – breaks   hear – here   principle – principal   capital – capitol
dear – deer   stationary – stationery   their – there   I'll – aisle

Campaign Promises

Rebecca and Jared are running for the office of student council president for Hoyt Junior High School. Their campaign speeches described to the student body what they'll do if they are elected. Part of their speeches are printed below. Read the speeches to answer the questions.

Rebecca: "If I'm elected president, I promise to get better athletic equipment, longer lunch periods and better career counseling. We need help right now in planning our goals for high school and college. I believe it is the right and responsibility of our student council to make this happen. And, if elected, I'll lead our council in that direction."

Jared: "I believe leadership is important to the work of our student council. We cannot be effective without goals. If I am elected student council president, I promise to work with the council to set goals that will reflect the needs of each and every student here."

1. What three things does Rebecca pledge to do if she is elected president?

   _____

   _____

2. What does Jared promise to do if elected president?

   _____

   _____

3. Which person made specific campaign promises? _____

4. What campaign promises would you make if you were running for president of the student council? Write them here.

   _____

   _____

Why do you think candidates make campaign promises?

Problems in the Sheriff's Office

Ted Wheeler may be the most honest and concerned sheriff Scott County has had in many years. For this, we applaud him.

His election campaign for his first term was promising. He pledged to restore honesty and pride to the department. We believe he kept this pledge. For this, we applaud him.

Most residents consider themselves more secure than at any time in recent years. For this, we applaud him.

This paper recently published an editorial. It said Wheeler is doing a good job. There is evidence, however, that Sheriff Wheeler has some problems.

Some employees have a complaint. They feel Wheeler's office doesn't provide the support they need. The employees fear they may be abruptly suspended if they make even a minor mistake. They're afraid they may be fired.

Employees say they're frequently treated unfairly by two of the sheriff's top aides. Sheriff Wheeler discussed the problem at his recent reelection dinner. He claimed this problem has been taken care of. His employees say they are still being bothered by the aides.

Other employees claim they don't have necessary supplies. They're frustrated with the worn-out radio equipment. Wheeler promised new equipment. Two months after it was ordered, it's still not available.

Basically, the workers are discouraged and irritated. They need support to perform well. They claim they're not receiving that support.

The *Daily Times* conducted its own investigation with Sheriff Wheeler's permission. We have now reached a conclusion.

Our conclusion is that most of the employees in the sheriff's office welcome high standards. They want to provide the best possible protection. But these workers are irritated by some barriers which prevent them from doing so.

Wheeler needs to remove these barriers.

The sheriff needs to examine the discipline policy in his office. One employee was abruptly suspended for being two minutes late due to car trouble. This happened after Wheeler promised that his aides wouldn't be so hard on the workers. Wheeler needs to question this action. He also needs to question the atmosphere this creates in his department.

Sheriff Wheeler needs to determine if the complaints against two of his aides are true. If the complaints are true, then the sheriff should take appropriate action.

The sheriff needs to examine what supplies the workers need. The workers are irritated because they don't have the proper equipment.

Sheriff Wheeler must respond to these accusations. He's made an effort to improve the department's image through honesty. But has he been completely honest with his employees? Has his lack of honesty destroyed the atmosphere of trust in the department?

Sheriff Wheeler, we invite you to respond to these findings. We know you'll do so.

86

Copyright © 1991 LinguiSystems, Inc.

Think It Over

Circle the answer that best completes each item below.

1. To get information for the editorial, the editor _____.
   a. interviewed Sheriff Wheeler
   b. conducted a survey
   c. listened to employee complaints
   d. invited Sheriff Wheeler to respond

2. Which happened first?
   a. The *Daily Times* published an editorial.
   b. Sheriff Wheeler ordered new radio equipment.
   c. Sheriff Wheeler took action against the complaints.
   d. Sheriff Wheeler responded to the editorial.

3. Sheriff Wheeler promised to _____.
   a. treat employees unfairly
   b. buy new automobiles for his employees
   c. take a vacation
   d. restore honesty and pride to the department

4. One complaint the employees have is _____.
   a. they're not receiving enough support
   b. the department standards are too high
   c. the editor should mind his own business
   d. Sheriff Wheeler needs more than two aides

5. The main idea of the editorial is that Sheriff Wheeler _____.
   a. should be re-elected because he's an honest and concerned man
   b. should be proud of his accomplishments but must handle some department problems
   c. is not very popular with the editor
   d. has two aides who should be fired

Fill It In

Choose a word from the list below that belongs with each group of words.

abruptly   aide   applaud   atmosphere   barrier   irritate

6. helper, assistant, _____

7. bother, annoy, _____

8. obstacle, hindrance, _____

9. suddenly, hastily, _____

10. mood, environment, _____

Word Window

Each of the words below contains the *ph* blend. What sound does the blend make? Read the words aloud and use some of them in sentences.

atmosphere	gopher	phase	physical
choreographer	orphanage	photo	telegraph

Just the Facts and Opinions

Editorials often express the opinions of the editor. But, they also contain facts to support the opinions. Read each sentence below. Then, decide if each sentence is a fact or an opinion. Write your answer on the line after each sentence. The first one is done for you.

1. This tea is too hot to drink.   *opinion* _____

2. This tea comes from China.   _____

3. Florida is very warm all year round.   _____

4. Florida is south of Georgia.   _____

5. Mr. Hancher wears gray suits.   _____

6. Gray suits are dull.   _____

7. Litter is bad for the environment.   _____

8. It's wrong to litter.   _____

9. This is a fast car.   _____

10. My car is newer than your car.   _____

Now, write one fact and one opinion about yourself.

_____

_____

Rescuers Hope to Save Fingers

Health / Science

Twelve seagoing rescuers are standing by on call. These rescuers hope to save Fingers' life. Fingers is a great blue whale. The whale watchers wait in boats off the Cape Cod, Massachusetts, coast. They hope to see Fingers. Then, they'll call the rescue team into action. The rescue team will attempt to save the 120-ton mammal.

Why does Fingers need rescuing? Fingers could die of starvation. The 85-foot animal is entangled in 250 feet of fishing line.

The line binds his mouth, his tail and one flipper. It's impossible for him to breathe, swim or eat properly. The line must be removed as soon as possible.

Last Tuesday, Fingers became entangled in 125 feet of fishing line. Volunteers worked for 12 hours to free him. The next day, he was as frisky as ever. On Thursday he encountered another line from a commercial fishing boat. He's been stuck in the line for the last four days. He has twice as much line tangled around him as before. There have been no sightings reported since Friday.

The seagoing rescue team is ready and waiting for a sighting. It will be easier for the rescue team to save Fingers if they tire him out first. Otherwise, Fingers will be too frisky to free from the line. The team may use special equipment and procedures to make Fingers too fatigued to fight.

Fingers has been a fascination to coastline residents since his first sighting in 1974. That's when he received his name. Someone noticed finger-like markings on his body.

Some tourists have made annual trips to the area because of Fingers. Their fascination with him brings them back year after year. His frisky nature and the finger-like markings give watchers an extra thrill when he's sighted.

Ms. Freda Williams of Pennsylvania says, "My first trip here was in 1979. I've been

back every year. Each time I hope to see Fingers. He's quite the entertainer. He simply amazes me.

"It's very depressing to think this mammal might die of starvation," Ms. Williams continues. "I'm grateful to the rescuers. They volunteer their time to save Fingers. If only he hadn't encountered the fishing line. I hope they'll think of a way to save him."

Anne Carnell is from Rhode Island. She joined the watchers on Friday evening. Ms. Carnell has studied whales for many years. She's concerned there have been no sightings in the last few days. She's afraid Fingers may be too fatigued to get free. However, Ms. Carnell holds on to one last hope.

"Fingers is playful," she says. "His disappearance may not mean he isn't alive. It's possible Fingers has freed himself. If so, he's on his way back to sea."

Ms. Williams stood on the coast looking out to sea. "It's sad to look out to sea and not see Fingers. This is the time of year he usually makes his appearance. But I just know we haven't seen the last of him. His disappearance doesn't mean he's gone forever. I'm sure our friend is all right. I have a feeling he'll be around to amaze us for years to come."

Think It Over

Choose the best answer for each item below. Circle the letter of your choice.

1. The rescuers were standing by in case _____.
   a. a tourist needed to be rescued
   b. some commercial fishermen needed their help
   c. Fingers became entangled in some fishing line
   d. none of the above

2. Which happened first?
   a. Anne Carnell came to Cape Cod.
   b. Fingers was stuck in fishing line for four days.
   c. Fingers became entangled in 125 feet of fishing line.
   d. A rescue team hoped to save Fingers.

3. The rescuers wanted to make Fingers exhausted _____.
   a. so he would be easier to save
   b. so the tourists could see him better
   c. because they wanted to capture him
   d. so he'll float to the surface

4. Some tourists' _____ brings them to the coast every year.
   a. business
   b. fascination for Fingers
   c. fishing
   d. both b and c

5. Another title for this article is _____.
   a. Plans Made to Capture Whale
   b. Tourists Return to the Coast
   c. Rescuers Hope to Save Mammal
   d. Commercial Fishermen Catch Blue Whale

Fill It In

Choose the word from the list below to complete each item.

disappearance   fascination   fatigued   frisky   seagoing   starvation

6. *Trust* is to *distrust* as *appearance* is to _____.

7. *Friendly* is to *kindly* as *lively* is to _____.

8. *Tense* is to *relaxed* as *energetic* is to _____.

9. *Dinner* is to *meal* as *hunger* is to _____.

10. *Purse* is to *handbag* as *amazement* is to _____.

Word Window

Say each of the words below. Then, tell what each word means.

disappearance   disconnect   dismount   displease
discomfort   dishonest   disobey   disregard

Dangers of the Sea

Whales, dolphins and turtles sometimes become entangled in fishing lines and die when companies fish for seafood. Write a letter to a seafood company expressing your concern. Give the company ideas for fishing without endangering other animals.

Dear Bottom of the Sea Seafood Company,

    I've read that dolphins, whales and turtles often get stuck in your fishing lines. I'm concerned

because _____

_____ .

    Your fishing practices aren't fair to the other sea animals because _____

_____ .

    When animals besides tuna are caught, it could result in _____

_____ .

    Some people have stopped buying your tuna because _____

_____ .

    Maybe you should think of different ways to catch tuna. I have some ideas that might help.

My first idea is _____

_____ .

    Another idea might be to _____

_____

You could try _____ .

    I hope this letter has been helpful. I hope to read about your new fishing policies soon.

                                          Sincerely,

_____

Burglars Steal More than Merchandise

Mr. and Mrs. John Taylor's home was broken into last month. Two suspects were arrested less than an hour after the burglary.

Mrs. Taylor of Friends Drive says, "Burglars invaded my home last month. But I considered myself fortunate. A tip from an unidentified caller made the difference. The Sheriff's Department recovered all the merchandise that morning."

Mr. Taylor had engraved his driver's license number on their possessions. Police officer Sally Jackson said this is an effective method and makes your possessions more secure.

"When police recover stolen items, they look for numbers that have been engraved on the items," Officer Jackson explained. "Engraved numbers are one form of identification. They help police identify the owners of the items. Burglars know this, so they often don't steal items with engraved numbers."

"Of course, we can't return all the items we find," Officer Jackson continues. "Sometimes we can't identify the owners. We store the items for a year. If no one claims the stolen items, they're sold at auctions. The auctions are scheduled four times a year."

The Taylors got their audio equipment, TV and all the other merchandise back. But there was still a loss.

"The merchandise was recovered, and for that I'm grateful," Mrs. Taylor confides. "But I still haven't recovered from the experience. I know that someone invaded my home. Things are different now when I come home in the evening. I feel afraid. I'm not sure things will ever be the same. My sense of security has been stolen."

Since the ordeal, the Taylors have installed a burglar alarm. "It's security, but it's a nuisance," Mr. Taylor says. "I

have to remember to turn it on. A couple of times I've come home with an uneasy feeling. I've wondered if the burglars have returned and figured out how to turn the alarm off. That's more than a nuisance. It's a frightening feeling."

The Taylors' feelings are normal. Many victims of home burglary typically have these feelings. A recent study showed that 60% of the victims felt "very much" or "somewhat less" secure in their homes. More than 20% confided they felt "very uneasy or panicky" for at least two months after the ordeal. About 60% of the people in the study installed an alarm system. This was an attempt to feel more secure.

However, many who installed the system confided they still had problems sleeping at night.

Dr. Grace Kerry is with the local mental health department. She agreed with the results of the study. She explained that typically, it takes victims about four weeks to recover from such an experience.

Mr. Taylor thinks about the ordeal when he leaves home each morning. Mrs. Taylor says she no longer feels safe at home alone.

"Make your home as safe as possible," Officer Jackson concludes. "Install an alarm system. Engrave your belongings. It takes time, but it's worth it."

Think It Over

Circle the letter of the best answer for each item below.

1. The suspects who burglarized the Taylor's home _____.
   a. were arrested
   b. sold the items at an auction
   c. engraved the items
   d. are out of jail

2. Which is not likely to happen after a burglary?
   a. Victims feel less secure in their homes.
   b. A victim installs an alarm system.
   c. Engraved merchandise is sold at an auction.
   d. Victims consider themselves fortunate.

3. Which of the following was stolen from the Taylors?
   a. TV
   b. audio equipment
   c. alarm system
   d. both a and b

4. Mrs. Taylor considers herself lucky because _____.
   a. she has a new alarm system
   b. her merchandise was recovered
   c. burglars didn't steal engraved merchandise
   d. her feelings about the burglary are normal

5. The worst result of a burglary is the _____.
   a. cost of installing an alarm system
   b. decrease in value after merchandise is engraved
   c. loss of feeling secure
   d. fact that merchandise is sold at auctions for a fraction of its value

Fill It In

Choose the best word from the list below to complete each sentence.

auctions	confided	engraved	invaded	nuisance	typically

6. My Aunt Betsy went to two _____ before she found an antique lamp.

7. These ants are becoming a _____!

8. I _____ ride the bus to work.

9. Rob _____ his problem to his counselor.

10. Darlene's fiance had her engagement ring _____.

Word Window

The words below are from Lessons 21 through 29. Read the words aloud.

apologize	unaware	stationary
sympathize (21)	unpleasant (24)	stationery (27)
buyer	selfish	phase
publisher (22)	yellowish (25)	photo (28)
inaccurate	formation	disconnect
incredible (23)	civilization (26)	disregard (29)

Burglar Beware

Mr. and Mrs. Taylor's belongings were returned because there was a tip from an unidentified caller. Burglaries occur at people's homes, at stores, at schools and at businesses. How can burglaries be prevented in these places? Write your answers on the lines below.

1. At homes

   a. _____

   b. _____

   c. _____

2. At stores

   a. _____

   b. _____

   c. _____

3. At schools

   a. _____

   b. _____

   c. _____

4. At businesses

   a. _____

   b. _____

   c. _____

Now, you've just returned home and found your home has been broken into. What would you do? Who would you call? How would you feel?

_____

_____

_____

_____

College Essential for Auto Mechanics

Twenty years ago, an ambitious young person could drop out of high school and become a good mechanic. He might learn a great deal working in the garage of a friend or relative. He might become an excellent backyard mechanic. There were good employment opportunities for the ambitious backyard mechanic.

"That's not true today," Airport Motors owner Fred Day says. "We're in desperate need of technically trained mechanics. The backyard mechanic won't do. The technology under the hoods of our late model cars is making college training a necessity.

"The manufacturer I buy from won't sell me parts unless I have qualified mechanics. A mechanic must be college-trained. He must take courses in technical English and applied technical mathematics. A student also needs to learn about electrical circuits and physics.

"Two of my best mechanics have returned to school. They're updating their training. They've enrolled in college-level courses for nine weeks. These mechanics are taking classes in electrical circuits and physics. They must pass these courses. Otherwise, they won't have the knowledge essential for comprehending the technical manuals for our new cars.

"After completing the courses, the mechanics will go to the manufacturer's institute. They'll study the technical manuals for new cars for three weeks. I still hire a few ambitious students who have completed a course in high school mechanics," Day admits. "However, without advanced training, they're limited to minor service jobs. If they want to make more money, they'll need the knowledge to comprehend technical manuals. That means enrolling in and completing college-level courses."

Airport Motors is like most major auto dealers. It's willing to finance the cost of enrolling in college courses for its more ambitious employees.

Carl Fine, owner of Fine's Auto, says one problem is keeping trained mechanics. "We don't mind paying the fees for an ambitious employee to enroll in college. The problem is that after completing the courses, an employee typically has many other job opportunities. It's very possible he'll have the opportunity to work for another dealer at a higher salary. In order to keep the employee, I have to increase his salary. Usually, I don't mind doing that. It's evident that he'll be a good worker.

"Since Henry Ford first manufactured the automobile, there's been a need for mechanics," Mr. Fine continues. "Job security for a good mechanic has always been high."

Input from major auto dealers makes it evident that some college training is essential. To comprehend the manuals and technology requires a degree from a technical school or junior college.

Day says, "We want college grads to work under the hood of our cars. They need the extra technical knowledge and skills. Otherwise, they'll be limited to changing tires and oil. We want to be the best auto shop in town. To be the best, we need the best mechanics in town."

Think It Over

Circle the best answer for each item below.

1. One of Carl Fine's problems is _____.
   a. he has to pay the required college fees
   b. once workers pass the courses, they'll have many other job opportunities
   c. there are no technical schools in his area
   d. he can't find trained mechanics

2. In order to keep a qualified technician, Carl Fine must _____.
   a. increase his salary
   b. pay his college fees
   c. limit him to minor jobs
   d. open a technical school

3. Good employment opportunities no longer exist for backyard mechanics because _____.
   a. their knowledge doesn't match today's technology
   b. manufacturers require dealers to employ trained mechanics
   c. they can't afford to go to college
   d. a and b only

4. Which sentence is false?
   a. Fred Day owns Airport Motors.
   b. Carl Fine wants backyard mechanics to pay for their own training.
   c. Mechanics who want to understand today's car manuals should attend college.
   d. Some high school graduates are hired by auto shops.

5. The main idea of the story is _____.
   a. backyard mechanics aren't ambitious
   b. managers don't treat backyard mechanics fairly
   c. the new car technology demands technically trained mechanics
   d. high school graduates can do only minor car repairs

Fill It In

Choose the best word from the list below to complete each sentence.

ambitious   circuit   electrical   evident   physics   technical

6. It's _____ that school will be canceled because of the snow.

7. The Smiths had _____ wiring done in their home.

8. Brian is an _____ student.

9. The bus driver drives the same _____ every day.

10. Physics is too _____ for me to understand.

Word Window

Circle the letters that make the *k* sound in each word below. Then, define the words.

archeologist   chord   chemistry   technical

archives   chorus   Christmastime   toothache

Get on the Right Course

Most jobs require special training. Look at the jobs in column *A*. Then, decide on the best training course from column *B* for each job. Write your answer on the line next to each job. You won't use all the choices from column *B*.

A	B
_____ architect	a. data entry
_____ editor	b. convention catering
_____ store manager	c. radio speech
_____ daycare center operator	d. advertising
_____ nurse	e. court systems
_____ computer programmer	f. drafting
_____ hotel manager	g. spelling and composition
_____ airline pilot	h. nutrition and health
	i. child development
	j. geography

Now, choose a career from the list above. Write your choice on the first line below. Then, list three more classes you'd have to take to get a job. Give reasons for your choices.

_____

1. _____

2. _____

3. _____

What career would you like to have after finishing school?

What are the hopes, problems, attitudes and needs of Danville teens? The answer to these questions will be determined soon. A survey is scheduled for November 3.

This survey is sponsored by local leaders interested in the city's youth. It's funded by local churches and private contributions. Michelle Gains is a graduate student from the university. She will conduct the survey.

The study was suggested by a Youth Concern Committee. The committee included church, social and racial group leaders. It also included elected officials. After meeting several times to discuss youth concerns, the group decided to sponsor the study. Reverend Carl Whitman explained, "We think we'll get a lot of honest information if we ask the youth about their concerns."

The committee asked the university for help conducting the study. Ms. Gains developed the survey questions at the university. Teenagers will have two hours to complete the survey. Computers at the university will be used to scan the survey response sheets.

"Questions on the survey will center on attitudes, career goals and social pressures. Interests and recreation will be surveyed, too," Reverend Whitman stated. "Teens will be asked how they spend their free time."

"We think the youth will find the survey interesting even though it will take two hours to complete," Ms. Gains added.

"About 300 students have already expressed an interest in the survey," she continued. "However, we don't want to survey just those who are interested. We'll be careful to scan all applications. We want a good sample of Danville's youth. If we choose only those who are eager to complete the survey, the outcome might be false. We might not have a true selection of all racial and social groups. We will select 200 students to represent the youth from all over the city."

Some citizens wonder if the students will answer the survey truthfully.

"I see no reason for the students not to take the survey seriously," Reverend Whitman says. "We're approaching it in a positive manner. We think the teens will answer honestly."

"We're reluctant to predict the outcome," Ms. Gains says. "For example, there's talk of building a recreation center in town. The center would be for local teens. We don't know if the teenagers want a center. The outcome of the study may confirm that it's a serious need. We can't now assume teens want a recreation center. Without the survey, we might build a center no one uses! That would be like a judge giving his verdict before hearing a case.

"The study may show that other needs of the youth are more important than a recreation center," she continues. "After the study, we'll be in a better position to give a verdict on the hopes, problems and needs of teenagers in Danville."

Think It Over

Circle the answer that best completes each sentence below.

1. Completing the survey will take each teenager approximately _____.
   a. two hours
   b. one hour
   c. two days
   d. half a day

2. Which will happen first?
   a. The response sheets will be scanned by a computer.
   b. The hopes and problems of teenagers will be identified.
   c. The students will respond to the survey.
   d. A recreation center will be built.

3. To make sure all youths are represented, _____.
   a. Reverend Whitman will conduct the survey
   b. 300 teenagers will volunteer to complete the survey
   c. youths will answer the survey in a church
   d. 200 students from all over the city will complete the survey

4. Michelle Gains was employed to _____.
   a. scan the response sheets
   b. conduct the survey
   c. build a recreation center
   d. choose youth to take the survey

5. Another title for this story is _____.
   a. Youth Concern Committee to Survey Parents of Teenagers
   b. Survey to Determine Needs of City's Youth
   c. Study Reveals the Need to Construct a Youth Center
   d. Reverend Whitman Creates Survey

Fill It In

Choose the synonym from the list below to complete each group of words.

outcome   recreation   racial   reverend   scan   verdict

6. examine, skim, _____

7. result, finding, _____

8. play, hobby, _____

9. minister, priest, _____

10. decision, judgment, _____

Word Window

Each of the words below have the *sh* sound. Circle the letters that make the *sh* sound and use the words in sentences.

appreciate   especially   physician   sociable

electrician   mathematician   racial   suspicious

Concern Commitee Survey

You've been asked to complete the Concern Committee survey. Answer each item honestly.

1. What do you hope will happen in your life in the next three years?

    _____

2. What do you worry about most?

    _____

3. Do you think students should wear uniforms to school? Explain your answer.

    _____

    _____

4. Do you think students should have curfews? Explain your answer.

    _____

    _____

5. If you could change one thing about your school or work, what would it be?

    _____

    Why? _____

    _____

6. What suggestion do you have for improving your community?

    _____

7. What is the greatest problem in the world today? What can you do to help solve it?

    _____

    _____

Is a survey the best way to discover people's opinions? Why?

The Last American Cowboys

"I can't explain it. I've never met a genuine trucker who couldn't wait to get home when he was away and who wasn't ready to go again once he got home." That's the opinion of Howard Settles. Settles has been a truck driver for 22 years. "We seem to have something in our blood that makes us want to keep on trucking," he adds.

You might think of truckers as the modern day cowboys. Truckers do a lot of rough riding. However, the comparison doesn't stop there. Truck drivers and cowboys spend lots of time away from home. It sounds like fun, but it's not much fun when you're out on the road.

"When I'm driving my 18-wheeler across Arizona at 2:00 A.M., I get lonely. I'm as lonesome as any cowboy out on the range," Settles says. "Sometimes, I talk to my truck like a cowboy would talk to his horse. There are times I feel lonely even when I'm in city traffic."

"Contrary to what some people think, we're not a bunch of brutes or rowdy rascals," Gene Turner adds. Turner's been on the road for 17 years. "Professional truckers have to be reliable. We drive $80,000 pieces of equipment down the highway. We need to be sure we don't make mistakes. We won't have the opportunity to make a second mistake. The first mistake may cost us our jobs or our lives. We take precautions. Even a minor mistake can cause our insurance to be more expensive."

Settles agrees with Turner. "We certainly aren't brutes or rascals. Contrary to popular belief, most of us are courteous drivers. Most of us sympathize with stranded travelers. We can recall times when we've broken down. We recall how grateful we were when someone felt obliged to help us. So we sympathize with other motorists who are having car trouble. And we feel obliged to offer assistance."

"Long-haul trucking isn't an ideal situation for a good marriage and a family," Turner says. "It's difficult to maintain marriage and family relationships. I've noticed more wives accompanying their trucking husbands. More and more women are becoming truck drivers, too. This is a great situation for many couples who don't have children at home. Many of my friends really enjoy having their spouses along.

"Some of the spouses take turns driving. This gives both drivers a chance to relax," Turner continues. "It's the safe thing to do. However, it's illegal if the spouse doesn't have the proper training and license."

"Trucking is a great business," Settles adds. "I've been around long enough to see some genuine improvement. Our trucks are much better equipped now. Having a CB radio helps relieve some of the loneliness.

"Some people say we're America's last cowboys," Turner concludes. "They say we would have made good scouts or explorers, too. I think that's probably right. And it's a great compliment!"

Think It Over

Circle the letter of the best answer for each sentence below.

1. In this article, a truck driver is compared to a _____.
   a. stranded motorist
   b. cowboy
   c. reverend
   d. rascal

2. Contrary to popular opinion, many professional drivers _____.
   a. are courteous
   b. are reliable
   c. sympathize with stranded travelers
   d. all of the above

3. Professional drivers take precautions to avoid mistakes because _____.
   a. a mistake may cost them their jobs or their lives
   b. a minor mistake can cause their insurance to decrease
   c. they want to be cowboys
   d. they don't want to get a speeding ticket

4. One improvement in the trucking business is _____.
   a. trucks have 18 wheels
   b. better equipment
   c. spouses without truck-driving licenses are allowed to drive
   d. insurance rates have decreased

5. The main idea of this story is _____.
   a. truck drivers are like cowboys who genuinely care about their jobs
   b. professional drivers try to avoid mistakes
   c. being a truck driver makes it difficult to maintain a good marriage
   d. more women are becoming truck drivers

Fill It In

Choose the best word from the list below to complete each sentence.

brutes   contrary   genuine   obliged   rascals   sympathize

6. While playing baseball, those little _____ broke my window!

7. David bought Lisa a _____ leather coat.

8. Mrs. Adams felt _____ to pick up the man's cane.

9. It's easy to _____ with people who are ill.

10. _____ to what you may think, I am not late.

Word Window

Say each word. Explain why the *g* in each word sounds like a *j*.

gem   gingerbread   stingy   religion
genuine   obliged   register   revenge

The Long Haul

Many truck drivers take long trips across the country. They often take the same route each time. Do you think you would enjoy being a truck driver? Complete the activity below to help you decide.

Think about the longest trip you've ever taken. Where did you go? What did you see along the way? How did you get there? What did you enjoy most about the trip? What was the worst thing about the trip? How did you feel when you finally arrived? Tell about the trip on the lines below.

_____

_____

_____

_____

_____

_____

1. Would you like to take this trip every week? Explain your answer.

    _____

    _____

2. What do you think would be the hardest thing about being a truck driver? Why?

    _____

    _____

3. What do you think truck drivers like most about their jobs?

    _____

    _____

Would you like a job that allows you to travel a lot? Why?

Theater Owners Oppose Law

Owners of local theaters are angry! They've vowed to take hasty action against a proposed law. The law would allow people attending movies to bring their own food into theaters. "No matter how you butter it, we are hot over the proposed law," one owner said. "People shouldn't be allowed to bring their own popcorn or thermos of soda. I foresee this being the beginning of some genuine problems."

Representative Timothy Looney is sponsoring the new law. "There are low-income groups in this state who can't afford to purchase the candy, popcorn and drinks that are sold at theaters," he argues. "It's unfair for those groups to have to sit through a movie without snacks. Snacks add to the pleasure of a movie. These people shouldn't feel like criminals if they bring their own snacks."

Looney's proposed law would allow each person attending a movie to take snacks and a thermos into the theater. "I don't foresee this being a problem for the owners," he explained. "The law would allow only those kinds of snacks that are already sold. Besides, plenty of people would still buy food at the theaters."

A committee appointed to study the proposed law has been getting opinions from different groups. Frances Burk, owner of a chain of theaters and president of the State Association of Theater Owners, appeared before the committee yesterday. She told the committee, "This will be a genuine problem for theater owners. Food sales are a vital source of income for our theaters. Sometimes we wonder if we're in the movie business or the food business. If this proposed law passes, I foresee one of two things happening. Either we'll have to raise the price of admission, or close our doors for good."

"Approximately 50 percent of the income from ticket sales pays for film rental," she continued. "Movie theaters are fortunate to break even on the income from tickets. We pay expenses such as salaries for our employees, maintainance for the building, insurance and film rental. For some owners, the only way to keep the doors open and make a profit is by selling food. If this proposed law causes a loss in profit, then our doors will remain open only if we increase ticket prices by $1.50. And if we do that, many people from low-income levels won't be able to attend the movie at all."

Fred Miller, a theater owner from Cleveland, was in total agreement with Ms. Burk. "Letting people bring food and drinks into our theaters would create health and safety hazards," he said. "We have to maintain good health standards when we prepare the food we sell. We know about its freshness. We maintain the cleanliness of the containers we sell food in. How are we going to know what is in a thermos that's brought into the theater?"

"I hope your committee understands all the complex problems this proposed law could create," he concluded. "I hope you're not too hasty in reaching a decision. I hope you understand that the cleanliness and freshness of our food is important. The wrong decision will harm both the people who own the theaters and the people who visit the theaters."

Think It Over

Circle the answer that best completes each sentence below.

1. Representative Looney favors bringing food into theaters because _____.
   a. foods served at the theaters aren't healthy
   b. the food sold by some theaters isn't clean or fresh
   c. people dislike the food that's served
   d. none of the above

2. If the law passes, one thing Frances Burk foresees is _____.
   a. raising the price of admission to a movie
   b. people bringing a thermos of coffee into the theater
   c. theater operators wondering if they're in the food business
   d. an increase in ticket sales

3. The reason Frances Burk foresees some theaters closing their doors is _____.
   a. fewer people would be able to afford tickets
   b. cleanliness and freshness of food would be a health problem
   c. the committee might be too hasty in reaching a decision
   d. they're tired of being in the food business

4. Fred Miller is concerned about _____.
   a. film rental
   b. freshness of food and cleanliness of its containers
   c. ticket prices
   d. the price of insurance

5. The main idea of this story is that theater operators _____.
   a. would raise the price of admission
   b. pay for film rental
   c. dislike the law sponsored by Representative Looney
   d. should be able to sell food

Fill It In

Choose the best word from the list below to complete each sentence.

cleanliness   freshness   theaters   foresee   hasty   thermos

6. A _____ decision could be costly.

7. Susan takes a _____ of hot coffee to work.

8. We like the restaurant because of the _____ of its food.

9. The movies at some _____ cost only $1.50.

10. The Post Office received an award for the _____ of its building.

════ Word Window ════

Each of the words below contains the *-ness* suffix. Say the words and use some of them in sentences.

cleanliness   fierceness   friendliness   recklessness
consciousness   freshness   hopelessness   weariness

════ How Do You Feel? ════

People have strong opinions about controversial topics. Imagine you're a theater owner. Write a letter to Representative Looney expressing your opinion about the proposed law.

Dear Representative Looney,

    I know you've proposed a law that states _____.

I am against the proposal for several reasons. My first reason is _____

_____.

    I'm also against it because _____

_____.

If the law passes, I might have to _____.

    Please consider withdrawing the proposal. Thank you for your time.

                Sincerely,

                _____

Now, imagine you're a citizen who is in favor of the proposed law. Write a letter to Representative Looney.

Dear Representative Looney,

    I'm glad you've proposed a law that would let me _____

_____. Even though I can afford to buy snacks at the theater, I'm in favor

of the law because _____.

    I'm also pleased with the proposal because _____

_____. I hope the new proposal becomes a law.

                Sincerely,

                _____

Name three controversial issues.

Is the Three-Wheel Vehicle Safe?

The safety of the three-wheel all-terrain vehicle (ATV) was placed on trial yesterday. Attorneys presented evidence regarding the safety of the ATV. More evidence will be given as the trial continues today. Mike Lawson is suing the manufacturer of the ATV for $3 million.

Lawson was seriously injured two years ago. He wrecked his all-terrain vehicle on a sand dune. He's now paralyzed from his hips down. He and his attorneys claim the design of the ATV makes it incredibly dangerous.

Lawson's attorneys called two expert witnesess to the stand. They agreed that the ATV is incredibly dangerous. Brad Tucker is a mechanical engineer. He was one of the experts called to the stand. "The vehicle appears safe to the average person," he said. "It just looks like a tricycle with big wheels and a motor. That's not the case. I believe the design of the ATV is dangerous. However, it's unreasonable to think the average buyer will know that."

Tucker used charts and graphs in his presentation. He also referred to physics. His presentation demonstrated how easily the ATV tips over. "And that's when the rider is traveling at a slow speed. Imagine what could happen at a higher speed!" Tucker added.

Brian Dixon was the other expert. He's an experienced motorcycle racer. "I did a safety check on the vehicle," he told the jury. "The way it bounces makes it difficult to control when the wheels are turned. The rider is constantly being bounced around. This vehicle is dangerous for anyone to ride. It's no wonder Mr. Lawson injured himself on the dune."

Dixon showed part of a demonstration film. In the film, the rider flipped forward after going over a six-inch bump. He'd been traveling at 20 miles per hour. "I agree with Mr. Tucker," Mr. Dixon said. "It's

unreasonable to think that Mr. Lawson could have avoided his accident. It's truly a calamity."

Pete Hogan is a defense attorney for Wheel Fun. Wheel Fun manufactured Mr. Lawson's three-wheeler. He disputes all claims that the vehicle is dangerous. He called several witnesses to the stand. The Wheel Fun safety expert was one witness. He brought surveys and safety checks that had been done by the company. He said the vehicle is the safest one on the market.

Hogan insisted Lawson's calamity wasn't caused by the vehicle's design. He claims Lawson was riding at too high a speed.

The jury will make its decision tomorrow. They may decide that the three-wheel vehicle is safe. Then, Wheel Fun can continue to sell the ATVs. However, the jury may decide that the vehicle's design caused Mr. Lawson's injury. Then, Wheel Fun will have to stop making the vehicles and give Mr. Lawson the settlement.

Think It Over

Circle the answer that best completes each sentence below.

1. Brad Tucker attempted to _____ in his presentation.
   a. prove Mike Lawson was paralyzed from the hips down
   b. demonstrate that the all-terrain vehicle tips over easily
   c. prove the vehicle is the safest on the market
   d. demonstrate Mike Lawson was riding too fast

2. Pete Hogan insisted _____.
   a. studies show that the vehicle is safe
   b. Mike Lawson had been driving too fast
   c. the vehicle is incredibly dangerous
   d. both a and b

3. Mr. Lawson was traveling _____ when he had his accident.
   a. 20 miles per hour
   b. at a slow speed
   c. The story doesn't say how fast.
   d. home from work

4. Brian Dixon says the vehicle is dangerous because _____.
   a. it's difficult to control
   b. Mike Lawson had an accident while riding the vehicle
   c. it's not as safe as a motorcycle
   d. the wheels fall off too easily

5. The reason this story was printed was to let the reader know that _____.
   a. Mike Lawson might win $3 million
   b. all-terrain vehicles can be dangerous
   c. that defense attorneys work for manufacturers
   d. Mike Lawson is paralyzed from the hips down

Fill It In

Choose the word that completes each list below.

calamity   dune   incredibly   presentation   all-terrain   unreasonable

6. disaster, misfortune, _____

7. exhibition, display, _____

8. unbelievably, amazingly, _____

9. hill, sandpile, _____

10. senseless, stubborn, _____

Lesson 35   108   Copyright © 1991 LinguiSystems, Inc.

Word Window

Congratulations! You've successfully completed *Times*! Read the list below to review what you've learned.

motionless (2)	survivor (8)	interference (12)	employment (15)
furnishings (4)	rebuild (11)	ex-senator (13)	they've (16)
agreeable (17)	wildflower (19)	inconvenient (23)	childish (25)
contentedly (18)	alphabetize (21)	unnecessary (24)	disappearance (29)
sociable (32)	freshness (34)		

Bikes and Tykes

Many different manufacturers make the same product. How do you know which one to choose? What should you do if the item you choose is faulty? What would you do in each situation below?

1. You've finally saved enough money to buy a 10-speed bike. But how will you know which bike is best for you? Rate the sources of information *1* through *6*, with *1* being the highest rating.

   _____ friends who have bikes   _____ bike store owner

   _____ bike ads in newspapers   _____ bike magazine

   _____ Consumer Reports magazine   _____ bike repair shop owner

2. You bought a model airplane for your brother. When he opened the box, several parts were missing. What would you do? Write a + next to the best choices.

   _____ Throw the set away since you can't find the store receipt.

   _____ Get angry at the person who sold you the set.

   _____ Write to the manufacturer.

   _____ Take the set back to the store and ask to see the manager.

3. Poorly made toys are dangerous. Tell what could happen to a child who plays with each toy below. Then, tell how you would fix each problem.

   The button eyes on a teddy bear aren't securely fastened.

   _____

   A pair of roller skates has a loose wheel.

   _____

Tell about a product you bought that you weren't happy with. What did you do?

Name _____

Student Progress Log

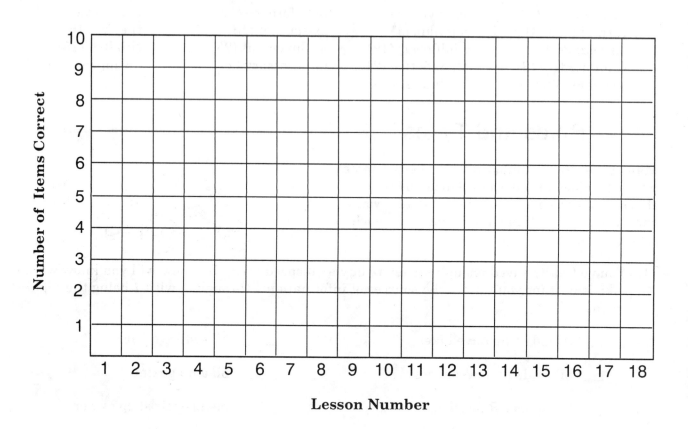

Lesson Number

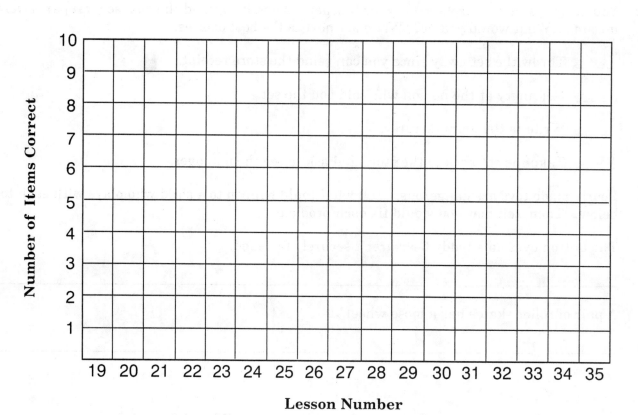

Lesson Number